THE PATH OF CARBON

IN PHOTOSYNTHESIS

THE PATH OF CARBON

IN PHOTOSYNTHESIS

By

J. A. BASSHAM, Ph.D.

*Research Chemist in the Radiation Laboratory
and Lecturer, Department of Chemistry,
University of California, Berkeley*

And

M. CALVIN, Ph.D., D.Sc.

*Professor of Chemistry, Department of Chemistry
and Radiation Laboratory, University
of California, Berkeley*

PRENTICE-HALL, INC.

Englewood Cliffs, N. J

1957

©—1957, By
PRENTICE-HALL, INC.
Englewood Cliffs, N. J.

Library of Congress Catalog Card No.: 57-12815

PRINTED IN THE UNITED STATES OF AMERICA
65288

The work described in this monograph was sponsored in part by the Chemistry Department and in part by the U.S. Atomic Energy Commission, University of California, Berkeley, California.

228

Contents

THE PATH OF CARBON

IN PHOTOSYNTHESIS

Introduction

Photosynthesis is the process by which green plants and a variety of related organisms are able to convert the energy of light (between 4,000 and 10,000 Å) into chemical potential energy. This process is usually depicted in chemical terms by an equation in which the reactants are the elements carbon, hydrogen, and oxygen in the form of low-energy compounds (carbon dioxide and water) and the products are molecular oxygen (for green plants) and carbohydrates. Thus, the electromagnetic energy on the left side of the following equation is converted, in part, to the chemical potential energy of carbohydrate on the right side:

$$CO_2 + H_2O + (h\nu) \longrightarrow (CH_2O)_x + O_2 \qquad (1)$$

As a result of considerable work in which a variety of methods were employed, especially during the last thirty years, this overall energy conversion equation is usually written in two parts in accordance with the hypothesis of van Niel. The first part describes the absorption of visible light and its conversion into two or more chemically identifiable species. Once formed, these species would liberate some fraction of the energy required for their formation if permitted to react with each other. There is considerable evidence for the association of this initial energy conversion reaction with either a direct or indirect separation of the water molecule of equation (1) into some chemical reducing agent, designated [H] in equation (2a), and a chemical oxidizing agent, designated [OH]. In green plants and other oxygen-producing organisms the oxidizing agent is then disposed of

1

by conversion to molecular oxygen which is liberated into the atmosphere (2b).

$$H_2O + E(h\nu) \longrightarrow \underset{\substack{\text{reducing} \\ \text{agent}}}{[H]} + \underset{\substack{\text{oxidizing} \\ \text{agent}}}{[OH]} \qquad (2a)$$

$$2[OH] \longrightarrow \tfrac{1}{2}O_2 + H_2O \qquad (2b)$$

The reducing agent [H] is used in the reduction of the carbon dioxide to produce ultimately all of the carbon compounds of the completely photo-autotrophic green organism. The present monograph describes some of the work done in our own group together with some of the related studies by others to gain an understanding of the photosynthetic reaction as a whole, and more particularly of reaction (2c).

$$CO_2 + 4[H] \longrightarrow (CH_2O)_x + H_2O \qquad (2c)$$

I

Definition

As knowledge regarding the formation of organic compounds from carbon dioxide and other inorganic materials in green plants accumulates, it becomes increasingly apparent that it is difficult to distinguish which transformations of carbon compounds should be classified as part of the pathway of carbon in photosynthesis and which reactions should be considered as other metabolic processes of the plant. All reactions of a photo-autotrophic plant rely ultimately on the energy stored by the photosynthetic process. Therefore, any definition of carbon reduction during photosynthesis based on a requirement of energy or equivalents of reducing agents should specify the requirement precisely. Even so, it is questionable whether such a definition can distinguish between carbon reduction reactions of photosynthesis and other metabolic transformations of carbon compounds. It is now believed that energy-carrying compounds such as adenosine triphosphate and reducing agents such as reduced triphosphopyridine nucleotide, which are formed during respiratory processes, also may be formed directly from products close to the primary photochemical reactions of photosynthesis. Transformations of carbon compounds which require such substances and which take place in the dark may also occur at a greatly accelerated rate during photosynthesis. Furthermore, most, if not all of the reactions of carbon reduction in photosynthesis are known to occur, although at a diminished rate, in the dark long after the immediate reducing and

3

energy-carrying agents formed from the photochemical reaction have decayed.

In the past it has been popular to define the pathway of carbon in photosynthesis as that sequence of reactions leading from carbon dioxide to some carbohydrate, usually unspecified. For simplicity this reaction can be written as:

$$CO_2 + 4[H] \longrightarrow (CH_2O) + H_2O$$

where (CH_2O) represents the carbohydrate and $[H]$ the reducing agent(s) derived from the light "reaction."

The attachment of special importance to the formation of carbohydrate as compared to fat and protein has stemmed from the closeness to unity of the assimilatory quotient, $-\Delta CO_2/\Delta O_2$, in measurements with a wide variety of plants, and to recovery from certain plant leaves of nearly quantitative amounts of carbohydrate based on their photosynthetic uptake of CO_2. However, the deviation of the photosynthetic quotient from unity need not be great to permit the formation of appreciable quantities of both amino acids and fats. The assimilatory quotient for protein, when nitrate is supplied as the source of nitrogen, has an average value of about 0.8, while the average value for fats is approximately 0.7. Observing photosynthetic gas exchange in *Chlorella pyrenoidosa*, Myers[92] found assimilatory quotients averaging about 0.75. This is in agreement with the frequently observed fact that *Chlorella pyrenoidosa*, growing in continuous bright light at photosynthetic rates which are many times their dark respiration rate, produce in some cases as high as 50% protein by weight and in other cases as high as 80% by weight of fats.

In spite of the above evidence, it might be postulated that a carbohydrate is formed first and then rapidly converted to other products. Fortunately, tracer experiments, to be described later, permit direct measurement of the relative rates of incorporation of newly assimilated carbon into the various products of photosynthesis. More important, identification of the actual intermediates in carbon assimilation and of the transformations involved make it possible to state at which points the path of carbon branches to give the precursors of carbohydrate, protein, and fats. Figure 1 shows that the only precursor necessarily common to carbohydrates, fats, and amino acids is 3-phosphoglyceric acid, the first stable product of carbon assimilation in photosynthesis. From this common intermediate, various transformations lead to a large variety of compounds including

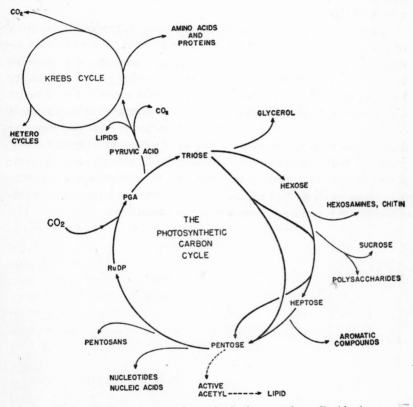

Fig. 1. Carbon compound synthesis from carbon dioxide in plants.

all the major plant constituents. The major storage products thus may be considered as essentially equal in precedence. It is true, of course, that fats and protein may be formed in the dark from carbohydrate, but the reverse process may also occur, depending on the requirements of the plant for growth and metabolism. The leaves of such higher plants as sugar beet and sunflower often incorporate most of their incoming carbon into carbohydrate, probably for convenience of transport to other organs of the plant. Nevertheless, production of fats and amino acids without the intervention of hexose intermediates in the green cells of even these leaves can be demonstrated by means of the tracer technique.

In order to arrive at some unambiguous definition of the pathway of carbon in photosynthesis, we will first define photosynthetic reducing agents and photosynthetic energy-carrying compounds as those compounds involved in transfer of reducing power and energy between the primary photochemical reactions and the reactions by which carbon is incorporated into more reduced or more energetic compounds. Those reactions which incorporate carbon into more reduced or more energetic compounds and which use photosynthetically produced reducing agents and photosynthetic energy-carrying compounds in order to proceed, together with intermediate and preparatory steps, such as hydrations, condensations, and rearrangements, constitute the pathway of carbon in photosynthesis.

II

Historical Background

---

1. EARLY DISCOVERIES

Following the discovery by Priestley (1772)[96] of the ability of green plants to "purify air," the recognition by Senebier (1782)[110] of the importance of "fixed air" in the nourishment of green plants, and the realization by Ingen-Housz (1780)[68] of the necessity of light for photosynthesis, this process was partially presented in chemical terms by Ingen-Housz in 1796[69] who stated that plants acquire their carbon by the decomposition of carbonic acid from the air, producing therefrom oxygen and organic matter. The participation of water in photosynthesis was established by the quantitative measurements of de Saussure in 1804[39] who showed that the increase in dry weight caused by the assimilation of a given quantity of carbon is considerably greater than the weight of carbon assimilated. Since the amount of oxygen evolved in photosynthesis is known to be equivalent to the amount of oxygen contained in the assimilated carbon dioxide, the increase in dry weight of the plant in excess of the weight of assimilated carbon could come only from water, taken up in some form which could not be removed by drying. After the recognition by Mayer in 1845[85] of the role of light as a source of energy for the photosynthetic process, it became possible to formulate the overall reaction of photosynthesis as a conversion of carbon dioxide, water, and light energy to oxygen and organic matter, containing stored chemical energy. Subsequent investigations of photosynthesis have

7

been concerned with the mechanism of photosynthesis and with the types of organic matter produced.

2. First chemical theories for carbon reduction in photosynthesis

The first chemical theory relating to carbon reduction during photosynthesis was that of Liebig who proposed in 1843[83] that plant acids are intermediates between carbon dioxide and sugars. This theory stemmed from the fact that these acids are intermediate in oxidation level between carbon dioxide and carbohydrate, and from the example of ripening fruits which are first acid and later become sweet.

This theory was disputed in 1870 by Baeyer[9] who postulated a reduction of carbon dioxide to formaldehyde (after a preliminary decomposition to carbon monoxide and oxygen) followed by condensation of the formaldehyde to carbohydrate. Of the two theories, the formaldehyde theory had the advantage of greater simplicity and a great amount of effort was expended in attempts to demonstrate a role of formaldehyde in the pathway of carbon reduction during photosynthesis. These efforts proved unsuccessful, by and large, and even where positive results were reported they were contradicted by other workers. Perhaps the most recent effort to determine the presence of formaldehyde as an intermediate in photosynthesis was carried out by allowing plants to absorb carbon dioxide containing a radio-isotope, carbon-fourteen (C^{14}) during photosynthesis, after which an extract of the plant material was made and mixed with a small amount of unlabeled formaldehyde. An aldehyde-trapping reagent (such as 2,4-dinitrophenylhydrazine) was then added, and the aldehyde derivative was isolated and its radioactivity determined. The amount of radioactivity found by this method was so little as to be insignificant compared to the measured radioactivity of other compounds identified as intermediates in carbon reduction during photosynthesis.

While the formaldehyde theory found little experimental support, the theory of carboxylic acids as intermediates in carbon reduction has proved to be near to the truth. However, the key compound, phosphoglyceric acid, was not suspected to be an intermediate until tracer methods permitted its identification as an early product of carbon fixation.

Although the theories of both Liebig and Baeyer would require several steps in the reduction of carbon dioxide, perhaps the first experimental evidence to indicate that photosynthesis is indeed a multistep process came in 1905 from the work of Blackman[22] who demonstrated kinetically that in addition to the primary photochemical steps, photosynthesis involved one or more temperature-dependent "dark" reactions. While some of these reactions are probably part of the oxygen-evolving mechanism, as suggested by Willstatter and Stoll (1918)[138], it is now known that many steps in the pathway of carbon reduction are such dark reactions.

3. SEPARATION OF CO_2 REDUCTION FROM PHOTOLYSIS OF WATER

(a) *Early Formulations.* Recognition of the complexity of photosynthesis raised the question of which reactions are photochemical and which are thermal, or enzymatic. Also the problem of whether it is carbon dioxide or water which is decomposed to give the evolved oxygen took on importance. For a time most theories postulated mechanisms in which some or all of the evolved oxygen came from carbon dioxide without passing through water as an intermediate. However, three lines of evidence, prior to the carbon tracer experiments, have indicated that all the evolved oxygen comes from the decomposition of water, the oxygen of the carbon dioxide being incorporated partly in reduced organic compounds and partly in water.

(b) *Classification from Comparative Biochemistry.* Photosynthesis was formulated by van Niel (1931)[129] as a biological oxidation-reduction reaction in which there is an intermolecular exchange of hydrogen atoms between water and carbon dioxide. In 1913 and 1914 Wieland[137] had depicted respiration as a transfer of hydrogen atoms from organic compounds to oxygen, while Kluyver and Donker

(1926)[76] postulated that various anaerobic fermentations are transfers of hydrogen to acceptors other than oxygen. Thunberg (1923)[126] suggested that photosynthesis also may be an oxidation-reduction of this type. Starting with the hypothesis of Kluyver and Donker, van Niel (1931)[129] compared photosynthesis in higher plants with photosynthesis of the sulfur bacteria and suggested that the two processes are similar, the hydrogen for the reduction of carbon dioxide being derived from hydrogen sulfide in the case of the sulfur bacteria, and from water in the case of higher plants. By 1941 when various types of sulfur and purple bacteria had been obtained in pure culture, van Niel[130] distinguished these organisms as members of several classes. For those organisms requiring light and inorganic substrates only, he wrote the general equation:

$$CO_2 + 2H_2A + \longrightarrow (CH_2O) + H_2O + 2A$$

(c) *The Hill Reaction.* Beginning in 1937, Hill[59,60,61] discovered that chloroplast suspensions, prepared by grinding green leaves in a phosphate-buffered sucrose solution and filtering through glass wool, were capable of evolving oxygen in the light, when certain iron-containing cell extracts were added. Later he found that the addition of ferric potassium oxalate to the chloroplasts was sufficient to produce this reaction, which has become known as the Hill reaction. Since that time various other oxidants have been employed, including quinone. While the Hill reaction does not necessarily have to correspond to a portion of the photosynthetic process, it is attractive to believe that such is the case, the photodecomposition of water by the two processes being the same and the added oxidant in the Hill reaction accepting the electrons (or hydrogen atoms) which in photosynthesis are used to reduce carbon dioxide. Similarities in the effect of certain inhibitors on the two processes, as well as similarities in kinetics and other physical properties of the two systems have tended to give credence to this hypothesis.

(d) *Isotopic Oxygen Experiment.* A direct determination of the origin of oxygen during photosynthesis was made by Ruben and co-workers[106] in 1941. Oxygen-eighteen was employed as a tracer element to label the water and the bicarbonate-carbonate at different levels. The composition of the evolved oxygen gas was determined and was found to agree with that of the water in oxygen-eighteen content and not with that of the CO_2. This experiment has been criticized on the grounds that there may be an equilibration of oxygen isotopes between water and bicarbonate molecules. It has not been possible to completely eliminate this doubt, but the results are consistent with other evidence indicating that the evolved oxygen has its immediate origin in the decomposition of water.

(e) *Carbon Reduction Reactions Considered "Dark" Enzymatic Reactions.* As a result of these three lines of evidence, there has been the wide acceptance of the theory that water is first decomposed by a photolytic reaction to give some reducing agent and some unstable intermediate from which oxygen is evolved, and that the reducing agent is then used to reduce carbon dioxide by one or more dark reactions. For the same reasons, the two hypotheses of Willstatter and Stoll[11] involving the formation and dismutation of performic acid from carbon dioxide and water were generally abandoned. Therefore, carbon reduction during photosynthesis has been considered as a process involving only enzymatic "dark reactions" of the type common to other reactions of intermediary metabolism. The connection between these reactions and the photochemical reactions of photosynthesis is believed to be that certain key steps of the carbon-reduction pathway require cofactors derived from the photochemical reactions and capable of carrying reducing power (electrons or hydrogen atoms) and chemical energy. The elucidation of the carbon-reduction mechanism became a problem of discovering a series of thermal, enzymatic reactions which lead from carbon dioxide through various intermediate compounds to the end products.

4. RELATION OF GENERAL INTERMEDIARY METABOLISM TO PHOTOSYNTHETIC CARBON REDUCTION

The development of the field concerned with intermediary metabolism, in particular carbohydrate breakdown, has proved to be of great importance in the discovery of the carbon-reduction pathway, although this importance could not be recognized until *in vivo* tracer experiments showed many of the intermediates to be the same. Thus, by 1940, the Emden-Meyerhoff pathway of carbohydrate breakdown via hexose diphosphate, triose phosphate, phosphoglycerate, phospho-enolpyruvate to pyruvate was described in detail. Each step of this pathway is now known to be important in photosynthetic carbon reduction to either carbohydrates, fats, or amino acids. Similarly, the pathway of pyruvate oxidation to carbon dioxide, described by Krebs and Johnson[79] in 1937 and widely known as the Krebs cycle, plays a part in formation of amino acids and other compounds.

It is apparent, therefore, that in order to establish the pathway of carbon reduction during photosynthesis a method was required for determining *in vivo* not only the reactions, if any, which are unique to photosynthesis, but also which of the many enzymatic transformations of carbon compounds already known are important in this process. In addition it was necessary to discover not only individual steps but also to place these steps in their correct relationship to one another. In view of the dual role of most of these enzymatic systems (in respiration and in photosynthesis) it would be impossible to identify photosynthetic steps and establish their inter-relationships from a knowledge of *in vitro* systems only. What was needed was a method for analyzing the transformations within the photosynthesizing plant which would take advantage of the differences in rate of reactions and direction of carbon flow through the sequence of compounds in photosynthesis as compared to respiration.

5. Development and Application of New Methods

(a) *Tracer Elements.* The separation and identification of metabolites as intermediate compounds in photosynthetic carbon reduction proved to be an almost impossible task, despite the efforts of many able investigators, as long as only classical methods of analysis were available. However, in 1939, Ruben, Hassid, and Kamen[102] reported a method of using the tracer-element technique in following the mechanism of carbon assimilation. In their experiments, the radioactive isotope, C^{11}, was used to label CO_2 which barley plants were then allowed to assimilate in the light and in the dark. It was found that radiocarbon was incorporated into carbohydrate not only in the light, but in the dark as well. However, when the leaves had been kept in the dark for 3 hours and then allowed to take up $C^{11}O_2$, no radiocarbon could be detected in the carbohydrates. Of the radiocarbon incorporated in the light, most was found to be in water compounds which were soluble and which were not carbohydrate, carbonate, keto acids, or pigments. Subsequent papers by Ruben and Kamen (1940)[103] reported investigations of the products of radiocarbon uptake by *Chlorella*. The early products of carbon assimilation were not identified but were found to contain a carboxyl group and one or more hydroxyl groups. Most of the incorporated carbon was found in the carboxyl group.

The early tracer carbon work was hampered by two factors. One was the short half-life of the C^{11} (22 minutes) which precluded fractionation procedures requiring long times. The other difficulty was the lack of suitable methods for separating the complex mixture of labeled metabolites which we know now is formed after only a few seconds exposure of the photosynthesizing plant to radiocarbon.

In 1940-1941, Ruben and Kamen[104,105] identified another carbon isotope, C^{14}, and discovered that it could be made by an (n,p) reaction from N^{14}. Thus, with the development of high neutron fluxes in nuclear reactors, it became possible to produce C^{14} in quantities which were quite adequate for biological tracer studies.

In 1947, Benson and Calvin[18] reported experiments in which C^{14} was employed to follow the dark fixation of carbon dioxide. This fixation was found to be greatly stimulated by pre-illumination of the plant (*Chlorella*) immediately before the exposure to $C^{14}O_2$. Also in 1947, Gaffron, Fager, and Brown[48] reported a continuous dark uptake of $C^{14}O_2$ by algae for periods up to 12 hours or more. By 1948, Calvin and Benson,[34] using extraction, precipitation, and ion exchange column procedures to separate $C^{14}O_2$ fixation products, found phosphoglyceric acid, malic acid, and alanine to be significantly labeled after 30-second photosynthesis with $C^{14}O_2$ or one-minute dark exposure to $C^{14}O_2$ following pre-illumination. However, the analytical procedures used by groups working with C^{14} were difficult, time-consuming, and in some cases led to contradictory results.

(b) *Paper Chromatography.* From 1941 on, Martin and Synge[86],[87] were developing methods of partition chromatography on inert supports for the separation of amino acids. In 1944, Consden, Gordon, and Martin[38] described the use of paper chromatography for the separation of amino acids. This method of analysis, which has been applied with modifications to almost every type of biological materials, provides a means of separating minute quantities of metabolites from very complex mixtures. Thus, there became available in the discovery of long-lived tracer carbon and paper chromatographic analysis the combination of techniques necessary to separate the chain of intermediate compounds formed by the photosynthesizing plant in assimilating carbon dioxide and to distinguish these compounds from other metabolites.

(c) *Combination of Tracers and Paper Chromatography Applied.* The use of two-dimensional paper chromatography to separate the amino acids formed during photosynthesis in *Chlorella* and *Scenedesmus* with $C^{14}O_2$, and the use of radioautographs to determine which amino acids were radioactive, were reported by Stepka, Benson, and Calvin in 1948.[116] Calvin and co-workers began to apply the combination of tracer studies and paper chromatography-radioautography to the separation and identification of other types of compounds. By 1950[16] a large number of compounds had been identified as products of carbon assimilation during short periods of photosynthesis (one minute or less) with $C^{14}O_2$. These compounds (amino acids, carboxylic acids, hexose and triose phosphates, phosphoglyceric acid, etc.) were all well-known from the field of intermediary metabolism. However, that two heretofore unknown sugar phosphates played an important part in carbon fixation was indicated by their early labeling during short exposures of unicellular algae to $C^{14}O_2$. These were identified by Benson[17] as ribulose diphosphate and sedoheptulose monophosphate.)

As various labeled products of carbon assimilation were identified, attempts were made to arrange them in some sequence and several hypotheses were proposed, until the photosynthetic carbon reduction cycle, involving about twelve intermediate compounds and as many enzymatic reactions, was evolved.[13] The work leading to the elucidation of this cycle may be considered under two principal categories: the first of these was the development of improved analytical procedures including chromatography, identification of radioactive compounds found on the chromatograms, and degradation of these compounds to locate the radioactive carbon atoms within the molecules. The second category pertains to the conditions of exposure of the plant to C^{14}. The two important types of experiment were: variation of time of exposure of the plant to $C^{14}O_2$ during steady-state photosynthesis; and variation in external conditions such as temperature, carbon dioxide pressure, and chemical inhibitors after previously allowing the intermediate compounds of carbon reduction to become saturated with C^{14}. Subsequent analysis of labeled compounds permitted observation of the effect of these variables on the pattern of carbon fixation in terms of the distribution of C^{14} among compounds and among carbon atoms within each compound.

III

Analytical Procedures

The literature on the separation of natural products including metabolic intermediates by paper chromatography has become very extensive in recent years and has been thoroughly reviewed.[23] The present descriptions will be limited to some of the methods which have been employed to study carbon assimilation and reduction during photosynthesis.

1. PREPARATION OF EXTRACT TO BE ANALYZED

(a) *Unicellular Algae.* In a typical experiment with unicellular green algae (e.g., *Chlorella pyrenoidosa* or *Scenedesmus*) one gram of plant material is centrifuged at 1,600 g., resuspended in distilled water, centrifuged again, and resuspended to a concentration of 1% (wet, packed volume/suspension volume) in $2.5 \times 10^{-5}M$ K_2HPO_4—KH_2PO_4 solution. (This small quantity of added phosphate improves the subsequent chromatography.) After addition of radiocarbon in the form of $C^{14}O_2$ or $HC^{14}O_3^-$, and a period of photosynthesis, the algal suspension is run into an amount of boiling absolute ethanol which will give a mixture containing 80% ethanol-20% water. The mixture is then allowed to cool and after 30 minutes the insoluble materials are removed by centrifugation. After decanting the supernatant solution, the solid material is re-extracted with 20% ethanol-80% water at 60°C for 10 minutes and the mixture is again centrifuged. The extracts are then combined and reduced in

16

volume with a water vacuum and heating not in excess of 35°C to 2 or 3 ml. This material is carefully transferred with alcohol-water rinsing to a conical centrifuge tube in which it is reduced in volume to about 1 ml. by evaporation with a nitrogen stream. The resulting thick suspension is extracted several times by mixing with petroleum ether (30-60°C boiling). The layers are separated each time by centrifugation and the petroleum ether layer discarded or saved for investigation of the lipid components. The aqueous layer is then ready for analysis by paper chromatography.

During the above procedures, determination is made of the amount of radiocarbon in the various suspensions and extracts. This is done by taking a small aliquot from each and spreading uniformly with drying on an aluminum disc. The radioactivity of the disc is then determined by counting with a thin-windowed Geiger-Müller tube.

(b) *Leaves of Higher Plants.* In experiments with leaves of higher plants, the leaf is taken from a chamber, after exposure to $C^{14}O_2$, and plunged immediately into a boiling solution of 80% ethanol-20% water. The leaves are broken mechanically and allowed to extract for 30 minutes. In an alternative procedure, the leaves, after exposure to $C^{14}O_2$, are plunged into liquid nitrogen and ground with a mortar and pestle to a fine powder which is then sprinkled into boiling ethanol-water solution. This method is recommended where the leaf is thick or for some other reason difficult to extract. In either method, the resulting leaf-alcohol-water mixture is treated in the same way as that described for the algae mixtures, except that an amount of phosphate buffer equivalent to that added to the algal suspension should be added to the final leaf extract to improve the chromatography.

2. Preparation of Chromatogram

(a) *Amount of Material.* In order to achieve good chromatographic separation of intermediary metabolites it is important that the amount of material to be analyzed be kept small enough to avoid overloading. For this reason the extract from not more than 20 mg. (wet weight) of plant material should be applied to a single two-dimensional chromatogram. Moreover, this material should include not more than 300 μg. of inorganic salts.

(b) *Application of Extract to Paper*. For most purposes, a sheet of Whatman No. 4 filter paper, about 46 by 57 cm. is used. This paper is previously washed by soaking in 0.5% oxalic acid solution for 2 hours and then rinsing with distilled water 10 times, after which it is dried.

A measured quantity of extract is applied from a dropper or micropipette to an area of the paper about 8 by 20 mm. at a distance of 60 mm. from each edge of the paper and with the long axis of the area of application (origin) parallel to the short axis of the paper. As the extract is applied to the paper, drying is facilitated by a stream of air which may be warmed, provided the area of application (origin) is never allowed to become completely dry. When the last of the extract has been applied to the paper, the air stream should be stopped and the origin left damp. These precautions are required to reduce the possibility of "sticking" of the compounds to the origin during the subsequent chromatography due to formation of complexes between the compounds and the paper. The paper should then be placed in the chromatography box or other humidified place to prevent further drying.

(c) *Development of the Chromatogram*. For developing the chromatogram, the shorter edge of the paper, next to the origin, is folded 2 cm. from the edge. The edges of two such papers are placed in a glass or stainless steel chromatography trough with a rod weight on top to hold them in place. The two papers hang from opposite sides of the trough over horizontal bars (to prevent siphoning) and with the origins below the point of contact of the bar with the paper (Fig. 2). The entire assembly is placed with the trough horizontal inside a vapor-tight box. Wooden or well insulated boxes with double pane windows are recommended unless a well thermostated room is available. The combined effect of a chromatography room thermostated to a 3-degree range (22-25°C) and wooden boxes is satisfactory

Fig. 2. Top view of chromatograms in chromatography troughs.

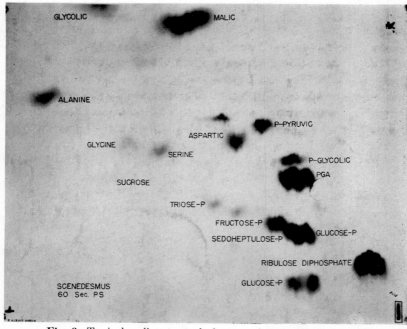

Fig. 3. Typical radioautograph from a photosynthesis experiment.

for maintenance of constant temperature during development of the chromatogram. In practice, it has been found useful to develop six to ten chromatograms in a single box, as the space inside the box then becomes quickly saturated with the solvent vapor.

After addition of 90-110 cc. of solvent to each trough, the box is closed and the chromatograms allowed to develop in the longer dimension of the paper. The solvent used in this first dimension is a neutral solvent made up of 72% freshly distilled phenol and 28% distilled water by weight.

After 10-12 hours the solvent has reached the end of the paper and the box is opened and the papers placed in a drying cabinet where they are allowed to dry at room temperature. The drying cabinet should be blower-ventilated to the outside atmosphere. The chromatography room should contain equipment to protect people handling the wet chromatograms from possible deleterious physiological effects of the solvent vapors. One solution to this problem is a helmet covering eyes, nose, and mouth and supplied with a stream of fresh air.

After drying, the papers are placed with their long edges (adjacent to the origin) in troughs inside a box used only for the second solvent and about 90 cc. of the solvent added. The second solvent, in this case, is made up immediately before using, by mixing equal parts of a solution of *n*-butanol (1,246 ml.) + water (84 ml.) and a solution of propionic acid (620 ml.) + water (790 ml.). The box is closed and the paper developed to the edge with this solvent (6-10 hours). The paper is removed and dried.

(d) *Other Systems.* It should be noted that the above conditions were chosen as the best ones for separating from plant extracts groups of compounds having widely different solubilities and occurring in greatly varying concentrations. There are better systems for each specific group of compounds (i.e., amino acid, sugar phosphates, carboxylic acid, etc.).[23] Moreover, if one wishes to obtain the best separation possible of phosphate esters with the above systems, one should allow the solvent to drip off the paper until two to three times as much movement of the compounds of interest has been obtained as can be obtained by allowing the solvent to travel only to the edge of the paper. The correct amount of time of development for this purpose may be followed by placing a small quantity of suitable mixture of colored indicators at the origin before development and observing their distance of travel.

3. RADIOAUTOGRAPHY

After chromatography is complete, the papers are each stamped at the corners with radioactive ink and placed in contact in the dark with a sheet of single emulsion x-ray film, to determine the positions of the radioactive compounds. About 10^{-2} μg. of C^{14} activity distributed over a 6 cm.^{2} area of the paper (an average-sized "spot") is sufficient to cause visible darkening of the film in 24 hours. This amount of radiocarbon emits 22,000 beta particles per minute, of which about 7,000 per minute escape from the paper, or 3,500 per minute on each side. With two weeks' exposure, 1/20 of this amount can barely be detected. This is nearly the limit of sensitivity of detection by this method, since the darkening of the film by this number of beta particles is just discernible above the darkening due to cosmic radiation.

After development of the x-ray film, the positions of the radioactive compounds on the paper are indicated by darkened areas, or "spots," on the film. The radioactive ink and the corresponding darkening of the film permit exact coincidence between film and paper to be made any time after development. A typical radioautograph from a photosynthesis experiment is shown in Fig. 3.

4. FURTHER SEPARATION OF OVERLAPPING COMPOUNDS

In some cases, two or more compounds may overlap in position, even after chromatography, and it then becomes necessary to elute them from the paper and separate them by a second chromatography. This may be accomplished by choosing a different set of solvents or by first altering the compounds chemically and then rechromatographying the mixture. Thus, in a typical experiment, the sugar monophosphate area, which is of considerable importance in the photosynthetic carbon reduction cycle, is eluted, the compounds incubated at 37°C with a phosphatase enzyme, and the free sugars rechromatographed on Whatman No. 1 filter paper with the two solvents described above.

5. IDENTIFICATION OF RADIOACTIVE COMPOUNDS

(a) *Position of Compound on Chromatogram.* There are available a large number of spray tests for identification of classes of compounds on paper chromatograms.[23] However, the amounts of material found on chromatograms of photosynthetic products are often below the limits of detection by these methods. Preliminary identification must usually be made by other methods. The position of the compound on the chromatogram provides two types of information. Since the stationary liquid phase is aqueous and the mobile phase organic, compounds moving short distances in both solvents must have strong hydrophilic properties while those which move large distances are more lipophilic in nature. Diphosphates of sugars are found quite close to the origin, while sugar monophosphates and phosphohydroxy carboxylic acids move a bit farther. Free sugars travel to the central area of the chromatogram in these solvents, while carboxylic acids and amino acids move from central to far depending upon carbon chain length and number of hydrophilic substituents.

The two solvent systems have about the same power to carry neutral substances; consequently, neutral compounds such as sugars and neutral amino acids move about as far in one direction as in the other and will be found somewhere along or near to a diagonal line drawn from the origin to the opposite corner of the chromatogram. However, since the first solvent is neutral and the second one acidic, there is a tendency for acidic substances to have their ionization repressed in the second dimension and consequently to move faster in the second direction than in the first. For that reason, acidic substances are usually found beyond the diagonal line in the second direction and basic substances short of it, these deviations from the diagonal being a rough measure of the compound's acidity or basicity.

(b) *Chemical Transformations, Rechromatography, Co-chromatography.* The subsequent clues as to an unknown compound's identity usually come from eluting the substance from the paper, performing some chemical or enzymatic treatment, rechromatographing, and observing change in position, fragmentation into several compounds, or loss of radioactivity. For example, an unknown compound, suspected of being a sugar phosphate because of its position near the origin is eluted, phosphatased, and rechromatographed, along with added, unlabeled known sugars (about 50 μg. of each). After development of the radioautograph, the paper is sprayed with a chemical solution which produces a color reaction wherever there is a carrier sugar compound. From the position of the unknown compound amongst the known compounds it is suspected of being a pentose. More of the original compound is phosphatased and run with various pentoses until it is found to co-chromatograph exactly with one of them. In this case, both the position of the radioactive spot and the details of its shape (as revealed by the radioautograph) coincide exactly with the color produced from the carrier by the spray test. If further confirmation of the identity is desired, a freshly prepared

Fig. 4. Chromatographic map.

unknown compound in the form of the free sugar is mixed with the authentic compound in solution and a derivative is prepared and recrystallized to constant specific activity or rechromatographed.

(c) *Chromatographic Maps.* By such methods, a large number of compounds, which are labeled as the result of carbon assimilation and reduction by plants during photosynthesis and respiration with $C^{14}O_2$ present, have been identified. These and a few additional related compounds are indicated in Figs. 4, 5, and 6. The small circles represent the centers of the areas which these compounds would occupy if they were chromatographed with a typical plant extract. It should be noted that the distance which acidic or basic substances will run in the first dimension depends on the acidity of the origin, and hence may vary somewhat from one extract to the next. The extent of this variation is indicated in Fig. 6 for some of the compounds by solid

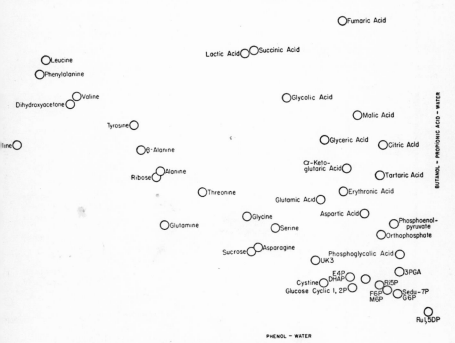

Fig. 5. Chromatographic map.

and broken circles representing more acidic and less acidic origins, respectively.

6. Degradation methods

It will be seen later that the intermediate compounds in the photosynthetic carbon-reduction cycle are all phosphate esters. Consequently, the first step in the degradation of these compounds usually is to elute the phosphate compound from the chromatogram of the plant extract, incubate with a phosphatase (purified to remove other enzyme activity), and rechromatograph to obtain the free compound.

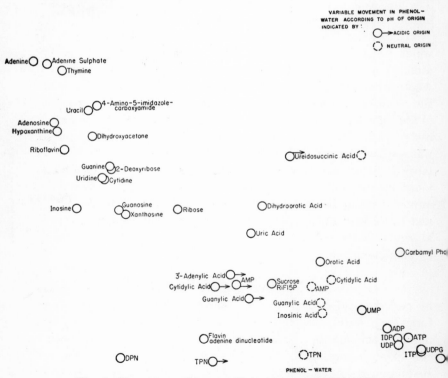

Fig. 6. Chromatographic map. Extent of variation of acidity of origin represented by solid (more acidic) and broken (less acidic) lines.

(a) *Glucose.* Glucose was degraded by Weinhouse,[131] by fermentation with *Lactobacillus casei* to lactic acid, followed by oxidation of the lactic acid with $KMnO_4$ to acetaldehyde and CO_2 (carbon atoms 3,4) and conversion of the acetaldehyde with sodium hypoiodite to iodoform (1,6) and formic acid (2,5) as described by Wood.[142] Aronoff[5] modified this procedure by oxidizing the lactic acid with chromium trioxide to CO_2 (3,4) and acetic acid, the barium salt of which was pyrolyzed to give $BaCO_3$ (2,5) and acetone which was converted by sodium hypoiodite to iodoform (1,6) and acetic acid.

Carbon atoms 3 and 6 were obtained separately by Wood[142] who employed a two-step oxidation of methyl glucoside with periodic acid. The first oxidation step gives formic acid (3) and a residue which on heating gives formaldehyde (6), methanol, and formic acid (1,2,4,5).

Topper and Hastings[127] developed a method for degrading glucose which involved two successive Wohl degradations to give carbon atoms 1 and 2. Periodate oxidation of the glucose gave carbon 6. Another portion of the glucose was treated with phenylhydrazone and the resulting osazone oxidized with periodic acid to give formic acid (4,5) formaldehyde (6), and the 1,2-bisphenylhydrazone of mesoxaldehyde (1,2,3). Part of this degradation procedure (with modifications) was used by Aronoff and Vernon[6] and by Calvin's group[19] to degrade labeled glucose and fructose obtained from photosynthetic extracts. Gunsalus and Gibbs[53] reported a method of degrading glucose in which fermentation by *Leuconostoc mesenteroides* gives CO_2 (1), ethanol (2,3), and lactic acid (4,5,6). The lactic acid was degraded as described above, while the ethanol was cleaved to formate (3) and iodoform (2) by alkaline iodine.

(b) *Fructose.* Fructose has been degraded,[13] as indicated above, by periodic acid oxidation of the osazone to give formic acid (4,5), formaldehyde (6), and mesoxaldehyde phenylhydrazone (1,2,3). Oxidation of the carbonyl carbon atom (2) to CO_2 can be carried out with cerate ion according to the method described by G. F. Smith.[112] Reduction to the mannitol by hydrogenation with platinum oxide followed by oxidation with periodic acid gives formaldehyde (1,6) and formic acid (2,3,4,5).

(c) *Ribulose.* Ribulose[13] was degraded by procedures similar to those described for fructose. Oxidation of the osazone with periodic acid gives formic acid (4), formaldehyde (5), and the mesoxaldehyde phenylhydrazone (1,2,3). Reduction to the sugar alcohol (ribitol) and then periodic acid oxidation gives formaldehyde (1,5) and formic acid (2,3,4). Cerate oxidation of the sugar gives CO_2 (2) and formic acid.

(d) *Sedoheptulose.* Sedoheptulose can be degraded[13] in part by similar methods. Cerate oxidation gives carbon dioxide (2), oxidation of the osazone with periodic acid gives formaldehyde (7), mesoxaldehyde (1,2), bisphenylhydrazone (1,2,3), and formic acid (4,5,6); oxidation of the sugar alcohol (volemitol) gives formaldehyde (1,7) and formic acid. In order to obtain carbon atom number 6 by itself, the sugar alcohol was incubated with *Acetobacter suboxidans* and after removal of the bacteria, rechromatography gave a small yield of guloheptulose in addition to sedoheptulose and mannoheptulose. The guloheptulose, which has the carbonyl group at the position that was carbon atom number 6 in sedoheptulose was then subjected to cerate oxidation, giving CO_2 (6) and formic acid. Conversion of sedoheptulose to the anhydride sedoheptulosan by treatment with acid ion exchange resin at 100°C, followed by oxidation with periodate gave formic acid (4) and a bicyclic anhydride from the remainder of the molecule.

(e) *Glyceric Acid.* Glyceric acid[12] was subjected to a two-step periodic acid degradation giving formaldehyde (β carbon) and glyoxylic acid which on continued oxidation with periodic acid gave CO_2 (carboxyl carbon) and formic acid (α carbon atom). This procedure was modified by Aronoff[4] who oxidized the glyoxylic acid with perchloratocerate to CO_2 and formic acid.

(f) *Other Compounds.* In addition to the degradations of compounds directly involved in the carbon reduction cycle (glucose is included here because of its close relation to fructose), a number of other compounds found to be labeled with carbon after relatively short exposures of the plants to C^{14} in the light have been degraded. These include alanine,[4] glycine,[109] serine,[33] aspartic acid,[33] malic acid,[15] succinic acid,[15] glycolic acid,[109] citrulline,[84] and others. The degradation data thus obtained have proved useful in establishing the relationships of these compounds to those in the carbon-reduction cycle in the overall scheme of carbon metabolism.

IV

Plant Material

---

1. VARIATIONS AND UNIFORMITIES

Before turning to the application of these techniques to the study of the pathway of carbon in photosynthesis, it is worthwhile to consider briefly the types of plants used in the experiments and their physiological conditions. Unicellular green algae and the leaves of a number of higher plants have been used most commonly for investigations of photosynthesis with tracer carbon and variations in the carbon fixation pattern have been reported. Moreover, chloroplast preparations have been used in some studies. Depending on the metabolism of the plant material and on the conditions under which the plant is exposed to C^{14}, widely different patterns can be obtained. Nonetheless, a survey of the products of short-term photosynthesis with plants of nine phyla[93] demonstrated a remarkable ubiquity of a number of amino acids and phosphate esters, including most of the compounds now known to be involved in the carbon-reduction cycle of photosynthesis. Despite greatly differing distribution of the labeled carbon among these compounds in one plant as compared with another, it seems likely that the carbon-reduction cycle is essentially the same in all green plants. It is to be expected that the flow of carbon from the carbon-reduction cycle to various end products will vary enormously from one plant to another.

2. ADVANTAGES OF UNICELLULAR ALGAE

In any investigation of a given metabolic pathway, such as the carbon-reduction cycle, it is imperative that the investigator have reproducible plant material to use from one experiment to another in order that he be able to compare the results of several experiments, each designed to bring to light a given phase of the rather complicated metabolic network. For this reason and others, unicellular green algae have been employed in a large number of studies. In terms of reproducibility, these organisms offer a number of advantages over higher plants. In the first place, there is a statistically large number of organisms so that the effects of individual variations are eliminated. Secondly, since these plants are microscopic and aquatic, they may be more readily subjected to uniform, nonvarying conditions of illumination and nutrition. Thirdly, the absence of nonphotosynthetic organs probably results in simplification of the physiology, although in this connection, it may be argued that an individual algal cell may have a more complicated metabolism than a single photosynthetic cell or leaf of a higher plant since the algal cell must carry out the organism's entire metabolism. However, there is a danger in using the excised leaves of higher plants for long exposures to radiocarbon since the metabolism of the detached leaf may be altered from its metabolism in the intact plant.

3. METHODS OF CULTURE

(a) *Species Used.* Two species of unicellular green algae which have been often used are *Chlorella pyrenoidosa* and *Scenedesmus.* Both of these species are capable of very high photosynthetic rates producing approximately 30 or more volumes of oxygen per hour per volume of wet packed plant material.

(b) *Importance of Reproducible Growth Conditions.* Methods of culturing these algae vary considerably from one laboratory to another, not only with respect to their nutrition, but also with respect to conditions of illumination, temperature, density of the culture, and the variability that is permitted in these several factors. Experience in carbon-labeling studies has shown that these variations affect the resulting labeled carbon pattern, in some cases causing important intermediate metabolites to occur in vanishingly small concentrations. It is easy to understand how an investigator unfamiliar with these variations might have some difficulty in repeating the results of others working in this field.

(c) *Media*. Several different culture media have been employed by the authors and co-workers in carbon assimilation studies[20] but the following one, reported by Myers[91] has been found to give algae with metabolic patterns similar in concentrations of intermediates to those obtained in the previous work by this group: To one liter of distilled water there are added 1.2 g. KNO_3, 2.5 g. $MgSO_4 \cdot 7H_2O$, 1.1 g. KH_2PO_4, and 1 ml. each of solution A and solution B, described below. The carboy of nutrient solution is sterilized in an autoclave at 121°C for 3 hours after which it is cooled and dispensed sterilely to the algae culture.

Solution A is made up by dissolving 59 g. of N-hydroxyethylene-diamine triacetic acid in 500 ml. H_2O, adding 24.9 g. $FeSO_4 \cdot 7H_2O$, diluting to 1.0 liter and aerating 16 hours. The solution is stored in the dark at about 10°C and used as needed. Solution B is made up by adding 2.86 g. H_3PO_4, 2.05 g. $MnSO_4 \cdot 4H_2O$, 0.10 g. $ZnCl_2$, 0.08 g. $CuSO_4 \cdot 5H_2O$, and 0.02 g. $H_2MoO_4 \cdot H_2O$ to one liter distilled H_2O.

(d) *Variable Density Culture*. Both variable density and constant density culture have been used for these experiments. In the case of the variable density cultures 1,100 ml. of nutrient solution is inoculated with a liquid culture of the species desired in a low-form culture flask (circular, flat bottom, about 25-cm. diameter) equipped with inlet and outlet tubes for adding nutrient and draining and for aerating with 4% CO_2 in air. The flasks are immersed in a water bath thermostated at 25°C, and illuminated through a transparent bottom panel by fluorescent lights (white, daylight type) which gives an intensity of 2,000 foot-candles at the bottom surface of the culture flasks. The algae are allowed to photosynthesize and multiply until

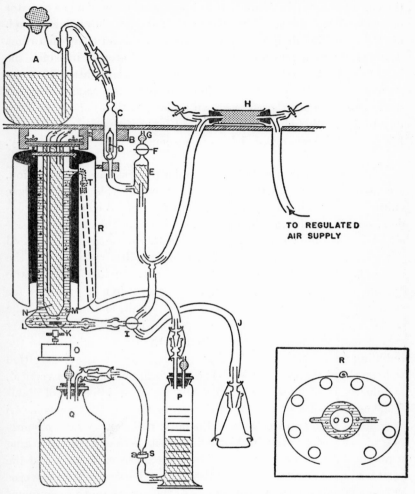

Fig. 7. Constant density algae culture apparatus: *A*, 16 liter carboy of medium; *B*, solenoid; *C*, glass tube with *D*, magnet; *E*, bubble trap; *F*, stopcock; *G*, cotton-packed air outlet; *H*, cotton-packed air filter; *I*, three-way stopcock; *J*, draining and inoculating tube; *K*, magnet; *L*, fin; *M*, encased algae culture; *N*, water bath; *O*, magnetic stirrer; *P*, collecting graduate; *Q*, reservoir; *R*, jacket with eight fluorescent lights; *S*, pinch clamp; *T*, overflow outlet. Inset is a cross section showing jacket with eight fluorescent lights.

the culture density is about 3 cc. wet packed volume of algae per liter of suspension. The algae are then harvested by withdrawing 900 ml. of the suspension daily and adding 900 ml. fresh nutrient each time. The culture soon reaches a "steady state" of growth in which the inoculum in the 200 ml. left each day is sufficient, after 24 hours growth, to provide the same inoculum in the same volume the next day. The algae are therefore grown under identical conditions from day to day, although the effective light intensity varies over the 24-hour cycle, decreasing as the algae suspension increases in density.

(e) *Constant Density Culture.* In order to overcome this variation, a constant density culture apparatus is used. In this case, the algae culture is grown in the space between two vertical concentric cylinders, sealed together at the top, the thickness of the culture suspension being 7.5 mm. (Fig. 7). Water at a thermostatically controlled temperature is circulated through the inside cylinder to maintain the algae suspension at a constant temperature. An inlet tube at the bottom of the space containing algae suspension is provided for entrance of nutrient solution and 4% CO_2 in air, and an outlet tube at the top permits overflow of the suspension and exit for the aerating gas. A magnetic stirrer at the bottom of the tube in addition to the bubbling action of the aerating gas provides the necessary agitation to keep the algae from settling. The tube is illuminated by a vertical, circular bank of fluorescent lights which give an intensity of about 3,000 foot-candles at the outer surface of the algal suspension. An appendage with two windows on the outer cylinder provides a thickness of suspension through which a light beam is passed before striking a photocell. The optical path between the algae suspension and the photocell may be altered so that the cell will be sensitive, in one case to the amount of light absorption, or in the other case to the amount of light scattering. Thus, the signal obtained from the photocell may be made to indicate either the optical density of the suspension or approximately the number of cells. The signal from the photocell is amplified and used to control a solenoid-operated valve in such a manner as to admit fresh nutrient solution to the tube when the density of the algal suspension exceeds a predetermined value. The excess algal suspension overflows and the density is maintained at a constant level. The overflow is not used for experiments, but rather algal suspension is drained out through the nutrient inlet tube, after which the tube automatically refills as the algae cells grow and divide.

V

Development of the Carbon-Reduction Cycle

---

1. VARIATION OF CARBON LABELING PATTERN WITH TIME

(a) *General Considerations.* In principle, the design of an experiment to follow the flow of carbon through a metabolic network appears simple, once the analytical techniques and identification and degradation of intermediate compounds already described has been accomplished. One should simply administer radiocarbon in the form of $C^{14}O_2$ or $HC^{14}O_3^-$ to an actively photosynthesizing leaf or algae suspension, and then, after a short time, stop the enzymatic processes by suddenly denaturing the enzymes. Subsequent analysis then shows which carbon atoms and which intermediate compounds have been labeled during the time allotted. If this kind of experiment is repeated for various exposure times, curves can be drawn showing the rate of entry of radiocarbon into the various positions and kinetic analysis of these curves would permit a description of the pathway of carbon through the network.

Such an attack has been used successfully but there are experimental and theoretical difficulties which must be kept in mind. In the first place, it is very important that the radiocarbon be introduced under conditions which do not disrupt the conditions of steady-state photosynthesis in the plant. The change from $C^{12}O_2$ to $C^{14}O_2$ should not be accompanied by any significant change in CO_2 pressure or in any other environmental factor. If such changes in environmental

34

conditions do occur, then it is possible that changes in concentrations of intermediates of the metabolic network may lead to nonsteady-state flow of carbon from one compound to another which is different from the steady-state transformation and which may obscure the normal flow.

(b) *Nonsteady-State Experiments.* In the early experiments with C^{14} in photosynthesis, such steady-state conditions were not always attained. *Chlorella* or *Scenedesmus*, suspended in weak phosphate buffer as described earlier, were aerated with 1 to 4% CO_2 in a thin, cylindrical vessel (called a "lollipop") mounted vertically between two bright incandescent lamps 1,000 to 10,000 foot-candles. After a period of about one hour, to establish a high rate of photosynthesis, the algae were flushed with air for 30-60 seconds after which $HC^{14}O_3^-$ solution was added, and the flask stoppered and shaken in the light for a few seconds. The algae were run into enough boiling ethanol to make a final concentration of 80% ethanol-20% water, subsequent analysis of the radioactive products being carried out by paper chromatography. In such an experiment, the fluctuation of CO_2 pressure obviously precludes the possibility of attaining true steady-state conditions. Nevertheless, these earlier experiments were fruitful in permitting identification of a large number of simple compounds including the carbon-reduction cycle intermediates which are labeled within a few seconds.

(c) *PGA First Product.* It soon became apparent that very short times of exposure to $C^{14}O_2$ were required to limit the labeling of compounds to the first few steps of the carbon assimilation pathway. When exposures of only 5 seconds were permitted, the predominant labeled product was 3-phosphoglyceric acid (PGA) while minor products included sugar phosphates, malic acid, and traces of amino acids. Degradation of the PGA from this experiment showed most of the radiocarbon to be in the carboxyl carbon and the formation of PGA via a carboxylation of some unknown two-carbon acceptor was suggested as a first step in carbon dioxide assimilation during photosynthesis.

(d) *Formation of Sugar Phosphates.* Triose and hexose phosphates were identified as early products and, after degradation of the hexoses showed a distribution similar to that found in the PGA, it was proposed that steps in the carbon-reduction pathway subsequent to the carboxylation included reduction of PGA to triose phosphate and the condensation of the triose phosphate molecules to form hexose phosphate by reactions which were presumed to be similar to, or identical with, a reversal of the Emden-Meyerhoff pathway for glycolysis.

(e) *Carbon Assimilation: A Cyclic Process.* Since the alpha and beta carbon atoms of PGA, as well as carbon atoms 1, 2, 5, and 6 of the hexoses were only very slightly labeled after a few seconds exposure of the photosynthesizing plant to $C^{14}O_2$, and since no labeled two- or one-carbon compounds could be found under these conditions, it appeared that carbon reduction in photosynthesis was a cyclic process in which some carbon dioxide acceptor was carboxylated to give PGA, the PGA was reduced to triose and hexose phosphates, and part of these sugar phosphates were then used to regenerate carbon dioxide acceptor. Discovery of sedoheptulose monophosphate and ribulose diphosphate among the early labeled products of $C^{14}O_2$ uptake suggested that these compounds might be involved in regeneration of CO_2 acceptor.

(f) *Studies with Leaves.* Because of the difficulty of obtaining exposure times of less than about 2 seconds with algae preparations, some studies were conducted with leaves and gaseous $C^{14}O_2$. In a typical experiment[13] a single excised trifoliate leaf from a soybean plant (var. *Hawkeye*) was placed in a circular flat illumination chamber with a detachable face. The chamber was equipped with two tubes, the lower one leading through a two-way stopcock to a loop containing $C^{14}O_2$. A loosely tied thread led from the leaf stem under the detachable face gasket, thence through a boiling ethanol bath and a glass tube to a weight. The illumination chamber was partially evacuated, both stopcocks were closed, and the clamps removed from the chamber, the detachable face remaining in position through atmospheric pressure. With the opening of the upper stopcock, the $C^{14}O_2$ was swept into the chamber by atmospheric pressure, the detachable face fell off and the leaf was pulled into boiling ethanol. An estimated exposure time of 0.4 second was obtained. The radioactive products were extracted and analyzed in the usual way. In other experiments, longer exposure times were obtained by holding the detachable face in position. The sugar phosphates obtained from the soybean extract were especially useful for degradation studies, since highly non-uniform labeling resulted from these short exposures to $C^{14}O_2$.

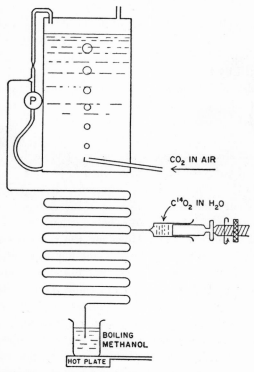

Fig. 8. Flow system for short exposures of algae to $C^{14}O_2$.

(g) *Steady-State Experiments.* In order to obtain true "steady-state" conditions during very short exposures to $C^{14}O_2$, an experiment was performed which employed a flow system for the addition of tracer carbon. A stream of algal suspension in 1-mm. transparent tubing was pumped from a large transparent reservoir into a beaker of boiling methanol (Fig. 8). The algae were illuminated in both reservoir and tubing, and the 4% CO_2 in air which bubbled through the reservoir was sufficient to maintain the dissolved carbon dioxide at a level which is saturating for photosynthesis in both the reservoir and the tubing, the time for the algal suspension to traverse the tubing being only 20 seconds. Thus, photosynthesis was maintained at an unchanged rate during the time the algae were in the tubing. At selected points along the tubing a solution of $C^{14}O_2$ in water was injected at a constant rate through a hypodermic needle, the additional CO_2 being a negligible increment to the CO_2 already present in the algal suspension. The time of exposure of the algae to the radiocarbon was determined by the length of tubing between the point of injection and the methanol killing and by the linear flow rate of the algae through the tubing (57 cm./sec.) and could be varied from about 1 to 15 seconds. The amount of radiocarbon incorporated into organic compounds in the algae was found to be linear with time of exposure, indicating that steady-state conditions had been achieved.

The rate of entry of radiocarbon into PGA was found to be the most rapid at the shortest times, in terms of both percentage of the total radiocarbon fixed, and in the rate of increase of specific activity (the concentration of intermediates being calculated by C^{14} "saturation" method described later). However, the rates of entry of radiocarbon into triose, hexose, pentose, and heptose phosphates were approximately equal, so that it was not possible to decide in what order these compounds occurred from these data alone. Therefore, these compounds were degraded as well as the hexose and heptose phosphates from the short-time soybean leaf exposures to obtain the labeling relationships between individual carbon atoms of these various sugar phosphates.

(h) *Distribution of C^{14} among Carbon Atoms of Intermediates.* The intramolecular distributions of radiocarbon found in the sugar phosphates and PGA are shown in Table I. For purposes of comparison, the distributions of radiocarbon in sedoheptulose from a 5-second and 0.4-second soybean leaf exposure are also shown. The possible error

Table I. RADIOACTIVITY DISTRIBUTION IN COMPOUNDS FROM FLOW EXPERIMENT
Scenedesmus obliquus, 5.4-second exposure to $C^{14}O_2$

Carbon atom Sugar, PGA	PGA	Fructose	Sedo-heptulose	Ribulose	Sedoheptulose from soybean	
					5 sec.	0.4 sec.
1, carboxyl.....	82	3	2	11	2	assumed 0
2, alpha........	6	3	2	10	4	assumed 0
3, beta.........	6	43	28	69	30	33
4..............		42	24	5	29	8
5..............		3	27	3	31	49
6..............		3	2		4	assumed 0
7..............			2		2	assumed 0

in these figures is about $\pm 10\%$ of the obtained values, but the important differences in labeling all lie well outside this error.

(i) *Formation of Fructose-6, Phosphate.* As had been observed in several previous cases, the distribution of radiocarbon found in PGA and in hexose phosphate agreed with the postulated mechanism for the reduction and condensation of PGA via a reversal of the Emden-Meyerhoff pathway.

$$2\overset{*}{C}H_2OP—\overset{*}{C}HOH—\overset{*}{C}O_2 \rightarrow \rightarrow \rightarrow$$

$$\overset{*}{C}H_2OH—\overset{*}{C}O—\overset{*}{C}HOH—\overset{*}{C}HOH—\overset{*}{C}HOH—\overset{*}{C}H_2O℗$$

However, it will be seen that in certain cases, to be discussed later, the distribution of radiocarbon in PGA need not be the same as that in the two halves of the hexose molecule for this relationship to be true.

(j) *Formation of Sedoheptulose Phosphate.* It can be seen from the degradation data that sedoheptulose cannot be formed by either a $C_1 + C_6$ addition or $C_2 + C_5$ addition, since the hexose and pentose molecules available do not have the correct labeling to form a part of the sedoheptulose molecule as it is labeled. A $C_3 + C_4$ addition was therefore suggested. Although a labeled C_4 sugar had not been found among products of $C^{14}O_2$ assimilation, it was believed that such a fragment might occur, perhaps at very low concentration, as a result of a transfer of two carbon atoms (1,2) from fructose mono-phosphate with transketolase. The resulting erythrose-4-phosphate labeled in carbon atoms 1 and 2 (corresponding to 3 and 4 of fructose) could then be condensed with glyceraldehyde-3-phosphate to give labeled sedoheptulose.

The labeling of carbon number 4 in sedoheptulose observed in the case of the very short periods of photosynthesis with soybean leaves seems to cast some doubt on the $C_6 \rightarrow C_4 + C_2$ split unless one can assume that the C_6 compound is itself not symmetrically labeled at the shortest times, owing to different specific activities of the two triose phosphates which react to give hexose phosphate.

```
  CH2OP            CH2OP                                    CH2OP
   |        2[H]     |          ——incomplete——              |
  CHOH     ——→     CHOH        ←—equilibration——           C=O
   |                |                                        |
 **COOH           **CHO                                    *CH2OH
  PGA               |↑
                  later, hence
                  more complete
                  equilibration          F-1,6-DiP
                     ↓|                      ↓
  CH2OP            CH2OP          CH2OH                     CH2OH
   |                |              |                         |
  C=O              C=O            C=O  ————————→            C=O
   |                |              |      **CHO              |
 **CHOH           **CH2OH —— *CHOH       |                 **CHOH
   |                         |           CHOH               |
  *CHOH                    **CHOH        |                  CHOH
   |                         |           CH2OP              |
 **CHOH ←—————————          CHOH                           CH2OP
   |                         |
  CHOH                      CH2OP
   |
  CH2OP
```

Degradation of fructose from the 0.4- and 0.3-second experiments showed no significant difference between the two halves of fructose. However, since that time, Gibbs and Kandler[50] have degraded glucose obtained from short exposures of *Chlorella* to $C^{14}O_2$ at lower light intensities and have found carbon number 3 to contain less C^{14} than carbon number 4, in agreement with the above postulation. Another possible route by which this inequality could be obtained is discussed on page 54 (Fig. 13).

(k) *Formation of Pentose Phosphates.* While the transketolase reaction proposed for the formation of sedoheptulose provides also for the formation of one molecule of pentose phosphate, the labeling of the resulting molecule does not entirely agree with that observed. Moreover, by the time these data were obtained it was also known from studies described later that ribulose diphosphate alone among the sugar phosphates appears to accept CO_2 in the carboxylation reaction leading to PGA. Therefore, it seemed likely that there should be a mechanism for the formation of additional pentose from heptose. There was postulated another transketolase reaction as follows:

$$
\begin{array}{cccccc}
\mathrm{CH_2OH} & \mathrm{{**}CHO} & \mathrm{CH_2OH} & \mathrm{{*}CHO} & & \mathrm{{*}C} \\
| & | & | & | & & | \\
\mathrm{C{=}O} + & \mathrm{CHOH} \rightarrow & \mathrm{C{=}O} + & \mathrm{{*}CHOH} & & \mathrm{{*}C} \\
| & | & | & | & & | \\
\mathrm{{*}CHOH} & \mathrm{CH_2O\textcircled{P}} & \mathrm{{**}CHOH} & \mathrm{{*}CHOH} & & \mathrm{{***}C} \\
| & & | & | & & | \\
\mathrm{{*}CHOH} & & \mathrm{CHOH} & \mathrm{CHOH} & & \mathrm{C} \\
| & & | & | & & | \\
\mathrm{{*}CHOH} & & \mathrm{CH_2O\textcircled{P}} & \mathrm{CH_2O\textcircled{P}} & & \mathrm{C} \\
| & & & & & \\
\mathrm{CHOH} & & & & & \\
| & & & & & \\
\mathrm{CH_2O\textcircled{P}} & & & & &
\end{array}
$$

SMP	Phospho-glycer-aldehyde	Xylulose monophos-phate	Ribose monophos-phate

This mechanism was made more plausible by the evidence for the reverse enzymatic reaction in other systems which was accumulating at that time.

If the various pentose monophosphates were then converted to ribulose diphosphate, the average labeling of pentose from the various sources would agree very well with the measured values.

(l) *Reversibility of Sugar Rearrangement Reactions.* With the formation of the pentose phosphates, the part of the carbon-reduction cycle accomplished by sugar rearrangements is complete, these rearrangements bringing about the conversion of five molecules of triose phosphate to three molecules of pentose phosphate. It seems likely that all the reactions involving the rearrangements of sugars are at least partly reversible during the time of these experiments. During carbon reduction in photosynthesis there will be a net "flow" of radiocarbon in the forward direction, but the possibility that the distribution of radiocarbon in earlier intermediates may reflect to some extent that of later intermediates should be kept in mind.

This type of equilibration between later and earlier intermediates seems to be indicated by the studies of Kandler and Gibbs[75] who degraded glucose obtained from *Chlorella*, tobacco leaves, and sunflower leaves after exposures to $C^{14}O_2$ and found in some cases more radiocarbon in carbon atoms 1 and 2 than in 5 and 6, and less in carbon atom number 3 than in number 4. It seems probable that the difference between the radioactivities in carbon atoms 3 and 4 arises from the incomplete equilibration between the glyceraldehyde phosphate and phosphodihydroxyacetone (discussed in connection with the sedoheptulose formation) which results in the condensation of glyceraldehyde phosphate with less radioactive dihydroxyacetone phosphate. The greater labeling of carbon atoms 1 and 2 (as compared with 5 and 6) is probably due to a back reaction with transketolase which takes the two top carbon atoms of xylulose, derived from the pentose pool (see Table I), and transfers them back to a tetrose fragment to give fructose. Thus there would be as a result a "labeling cycle" in which carbon atoms 3 and 4 of fructose would be successively 1 and 2 of tetrose, 4 and 5 of sedoheptulose, 1 and 2 of ribose, then ribulose and xylulose, and finally 1 and 2 of fructose. The occurrence of this type of back reaction may be accentuated in some cases by nonsteady-state conditions which result in rapid fluctuations in concentrations of intermediates and which might, in extreme cases, even cause a momentary reversal in the direction of net flow of carbon.

In general, the conditions under which such back labeling from pentose to hexose should be accentuated are those in which the rate of removal of pentose by carboxylation is for some reason diminished (either by lack of sufficient carboxydismutase or by an added relatively specific inhibitor). This would result in an increase in the concentrations of first pentose phosphate and then heptose and hexose phosphates. Since all the sugar rearrangement reactions are reversible and since the rates of these reactions are generally first order with respect to the sugar phosphate concentrations, both back and for-

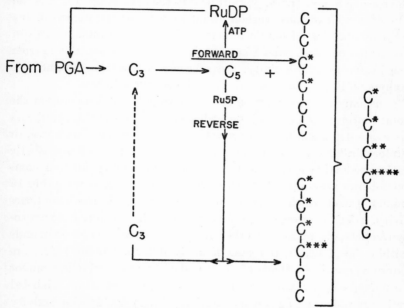

Fig. 9. Redistribution of carbon in sugar rearrangement; for details see Fig. 13.

wards reactions would be accelerated. Indeed, this seems to be the case of the experiments reported by Gibbs and Kandler,[50] in which the RuDP and hexose monophosphate radioactivity dominates a 1 minute photosynthesis chromatogram from *Chlorella*. This "reverse labeling" is illustrated in Fig. 9.

2. CARBON-FOURTEEN SATURATION EXPERIMENTS: CHANGES IN STEADY STATE AND TRANSIENTS

(a) *General Considerations.* The carbon labeling experiments described above all were carried out with short exposures to $C^{14}O_2$ to obtain selective labeling of compounds and carbon atoms. Quite different information can be obtained by allowing the plant to photosynthesize with radiocarbon until all the carbon atoms of the intermediate compounds are saturated with C^{14}. This is achieved when the specific radioactivity, proportional to the percentage of C^{14}, is the same for each of these carbon atoms as it is for the carbon of the labeled CO_2. Then, from the amount of radioactivity found in a given compound obtained from a known amount of cell material, and from the known specific activity, the concentration of the intermediate compound in the plant material may be calculated.

In many cases, it may be necessary to differentiate between the total concentration of the intermediate compounds in the plant, and its concentration within an actively turning over metabolic pool, or "reservoir." In the case of intermediates in the photosynthetic carbon-reduction cycle, the total radioactivity found in each compound rises very rapidly, reaching a nearly constant value within 15 minutes, after which there is a much slower gradual rise in radioactivity. It is, therefore, quite easy to distinguish between active photosynthetic cycle pools and other reservoirs of the same compounds within the plant. In the case of many other compounds that are intermediates in synthesis of plant materials, this distinction cannot be made so easily, even when the compound in question is labeled rather rapidly, and both concentration changes and specific activity changes then must be kept in mind when interpreting measured change in total radioactivity within a given substance.

While the measurement of the concentrations of compounds in "active" metabolic pools provides useful information, it is even more profitable after establishing and measuring a steady-state condition, to change some environmental factor and measure the resulting new steady state and the transient conditions which occur in going from one steady-state condition to another.

(b) *Apparatus.* The usual procedure employed in such studies requires a closed system through which gas is circulated by means of a pump and passes through a thin transparent cell which contains algae suspension, and through a system of tubing, stopcocks, and flasks which permits adjustment of the system to large or small gas volume, and provides for addition of a reservoir of $C^{14}O_2$ to the system. The cell containing the algae suspension is equipped with a stopcock to permit removal of aliquot samples of the suspension during the course of the experiment without interrupting the circulation of the gas through the algae. The cell is water-jacketed and the light beam used to illuminate the algae during photosynthesis passes through a water-cooled sheet of infrared-absorbing glass.

Additional items of equipment which are useful but not essential for this particular experiment include a CO_2 analyzer, an O_2 analyzer, and an ionization chamber connected to a vibrating reed electrometer. The signals from these instruments are recorded continuously on a multipoint recorder. The rates of change of CO_2, O_2, and $C^{14}O_2$ with time are used to measure the rates of photosynthesis and respiration during the course of the experiment, and these measurements later may be correlated with other results of the experiment.

When the condition to be varied is CO_2 pressure, an auxiliary system containing labeled CO_2 at the same specific activity but at a lower partial pressure in air must be provided, and provision must be made for switching the algae suspension cell from the high CO_2 pressure system to the low CO_2 system.

(c) *Method. Scenedesmus* or *Chlorella*, grown according to conditions already described, are centrifuged from their nutrient solutions and resuspended in phosphate buffer. The suspension is placed in the illumination cell and a mixture of 1 to 2% CO_2 in air is passed through the system, with the light on. The system is then closed, and with the volume of the system small (about 300 cc.), the rate of photosynthesis is determined. The volume of the system is then increased by connecting a 5-liter flask, after which $C^{14}O_2$ of known amount and specific activity is introduced into the system by connecting with another small flask. An hour of photosynthesis with radiocarbon is permitted to insure C^{14} saturation of various intermediates. At this point the system may be made small again by temporarily closing off the 5-liter flask and the rate of photosynthesis again determined in terms of CO_2 uptake, $C^{14}O_2$ uptake, and O_2 evolution. The 5-liter flask is again connected to the system and a few minutes allowed to re-establish the steady-state conditions.

Several aliquot samples of the algae suspension (about 1 ml.) are then taken, each being run into a weighed tube containing 2 ml. methanol at room temperature. This method of killing the algae has been found to be effective within 1 second. The tubes are later weighed again to determine the exact size of each sample. Subsequent extraction and analysis of the radioactive compounds in the plant material are performed in the same manner as described earlier, but the entire extract from each sample is used for a single chromatogram.

Radioautographs of the chromatograms are made and the radio-activity of each individual compound of interest is determined by counting directly on the paper chromatogram with a thin-window Geiger-Müller tube. Absorption of radiation in the paper decreases the sensitivity of the counting method but the factor by which it is decreased is constant for the various compounds with a given radioactive isotope and can be easily determined (it is about three for C^{14} and Whatman No. 4 paper, using 1.0-mg./cm.^{2} window tubes with a sensitivity of 1 count for 6 disintegrations). From the known specific activity of the CO_2 used, and from the radioactivity found in a given compound from a known amount of plant material, the concentration of the active pool of the compound in the plant can be calculated.

After several samples have been taken to measure the original steady state, some change is made in the environment (such as turning off the light) and samples are taken, very rapidly at first in order to detect transient changes, and then more slowly in order to observe the establishment of the new steady state. A suitable draining-stopcock for taking rapid samples is a three-way, equilateral stopcock in which any two of the three ports may be connected at a given time. One port is connected to the cell containing the algae, one port is connected to the incoming gas, and one port is open. When a sample is taken the port leading to the cell, which is under slight positive pressure, is connected to the open port for about 0.5 second. The stopcock is then rotated rapidly 120°, passing quickly the point at which the circulating gas port connects with the open port (to flush the algae suspension from the stopcock) and then connecting the gas port with the algae cell, thus keeping the stopcock and entrance tube to the cell free of algae suspension except during draining. A constricted bypass tube from the incoming gas line to the algae cell provides an alternate route for gas flow while a sample is being taken, thus insuring continuous aeration of the algae. In this way it is possible to take samples every two seconds.

(d) *Light-Dark Changes.* The first change in steady state to be studied was the change from photosynthesis in the light to a condition of darkness.[35] The concentrations of some photosynthetic intermediate compounds in carbon reduction found in the light and in the dark in a later experiment[14] are shown in Table II. It can be seen

Table II. STEADY STATE CONCENTRATIONS OF PHOTOSYNTHETIC INTERMEDIATES AND RELATED HEXOSE PHOSPHATES (in μmoles/cc. of algae)

Compound	Light	Dark	Change
Phosphoglyceric acid...........	1.63	2.42	+0.79
Ribulose diphosphate.........	0.51	less than 0.0005	−0.51
Pentose monophosphates......	0.17	0.08	−0.09
Sedoheptulose diphosphate*....	0.006	0.006	0
Fructose diphosphate.........	0.004	0.001	−0.003
Fructose-6-phosphate.........	0.12	0.12	0
Glucose diphosphate..........	0.003	0.003	0
Glucose-6-phosphate..........	0.33	0.37	+0.04
Triose phosphate area.........	0.21	0.12	−0.09

* Sedoheptulose monophosphate was present but not measured in this experiment because of suspected contamination with mannose phosphate.

that the most pronounced changes that occur in going from light to dark are the increase in phosphoglyceric acid and the decrease in ribulose diphosphate. The decrease in triose phosphate and pentose phosphate areas should also be noted.

The changes in concentrations of phosphoglyceric acid and ribulose diphosphate as a function of time after the light is turned off are shown in Fig. 10. From these results it is easy to conclude that the carboxylation reaction by which PGA is formed is a dark reaction which does not require any cofactors derived from light energy but that the reaction by which PGA is reduced to triose phosphate is a reaction which does require such cofactors.

The oxidation of glyceraldehyde-3-phosphate to diphosphoglyceric acid by triose phosphate dehydrogenase in other systems was known to be accompanied by the reduction of either diphosphopyridine nucleotide (DPN) or triphosphopyridine nucleotide (TPN) to the corresponding reduced coenzyme. Moreover, the conversion of diphosphoglyceric acid to PGA was known to be accompanied by formation of adenosine triphosphate (ATP) from adenosine diphosphate (ADP). Therefore, it was suggested that in photosynthetic reduction of carbon dioxide, PGA was reduced to glyceraldehyde phosphate by enzymatic reactions analogous to the reverse reactions already known, and that the reduction of each PGA molecule required the conversion of one molecule of reduced TPN (or DPN or some as yet unknown cofactor of about the same reduction potential) to the oxidized form of the cofactor and the conversion of one molecule of ATP to ADP and inorganic phosphate. It was proposed that reduced and energetic

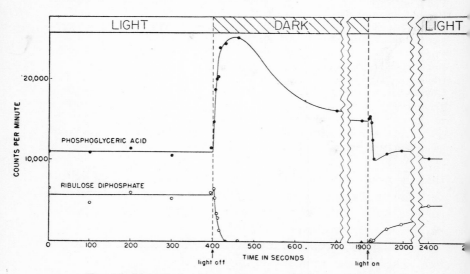

Fig. 10. Light-dark changes in concentrations of PGA and RuDP.

forms of these cofactors were derived from the photochemical reactions of photosynthesis. The reservoirs of the cofactors were presumed to be so small that the supply of these compounds was exhausted very soon after the light was turned off. Consequently, although the reaction by which PGA was formed would continue until the supply of carbon dioxide acceptor was exhausted, the reaction by which PGA was used up should stop soon after the light was turned off. The initial rate of increase in the concentration of PGA should be equal to the steady-state rate of formation of PGA.

The rapid decrease in ribulose diphosphate concentration on turning off the light had suggested that it might be the acceptor of carbon dioxide in a reaction leading to the formation of either one or two

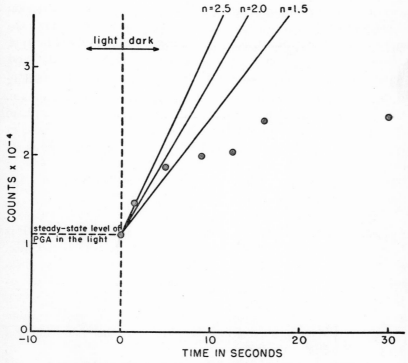

Fig. 11. Rate increase of PGA in the dark after the light is turned off.

molecules of PGA, and this suggestion was supported by studies of steady-state changes accompanying changes in CO_2 pressure described later. Therefore, it was of interest to compare the initial rate of change in PGA concentration on turning off the light with the rate of entry of CO_2. This comparison is made in Fig. 11.

The letter n denotes the straight lines which correspond to various theoretical rates of change of PGA in moles per second compared with one mole per second of CO_2 taken up as measured during the period of photosynthesis just preceding turning off the light. The circles are the experimentally determined PGA concentrations. While the rate of increase of PGA soon falls off owing to the drop in ribulose diphosphate concentration, it is clear that during the first 4 seconds the rate of change of PGA in moles per unit time is 2.0 ± 0.5 times the rate of uptake of CO_2 during photosynthesis. Thus, there is provided evidence for the formation *in vivo* of two molecules of PGA from one molecule of ribulose diphosphate and one molecule of CO_2 (or HCO_3^-).

The formation of ribulose diphosphate was presumed to require ATP as a cofactor by analogy with the enzymatic reaction leading to the formation of fructose diphosphate from fructose-6-phosphate. The *in vitro* enzymatic formation of RuDP from ribulose-5-phosphate (RuMP) has been found to require ATP. Therefore, the decrease in concentration of ribulose diphosphate (RuDP) was explained as resulting from its continued carboxylation coupled with a decrease in its rate of formation resulting from a decrease in the supply of ATP, derived from photochemical reactions.

The concentration of pentose monophosphates might be expected to increase if the reaction by which they are converted to RuDP is blocked on turning off the light, whereas the opposite is the case. However, it must be kept in mind that the formation of triose phosphates by reduction of PGA stops when the light is turned off, resulting in a drop in concentration (Table II) of triose phosphates which are precursors of the pentose monophosphates. The concentration changes of the pentose monophosphate are apparently most affected by this drop in precursor concentration.

It is interesting to note that the concentrations of the hexose and heptose phosphates were found to be virtually unaffected by turning off the light in the case studied. These compounds are formed by aldolase reactions from triose phosphate and are used up by trans-ketolase reactions also requiring triose phosphates. Thus, a decrease in triose phosphate concentrations apparently produces no net effect on the hexose and heptose monophosphates. Moreover, the break-down of these hexose and heptose monophosphates to trioses and tetrose phosphates by aldolase requires a preliminary formation of the diphosphates with ATP, a cofactor which appears to be reduced in concentration in the dark in the subcellular compartment contain-ing the carbon-reduction cycle system.

(e) *High CO₂-Low CO₂ Pressure Changes.* Transient changes and

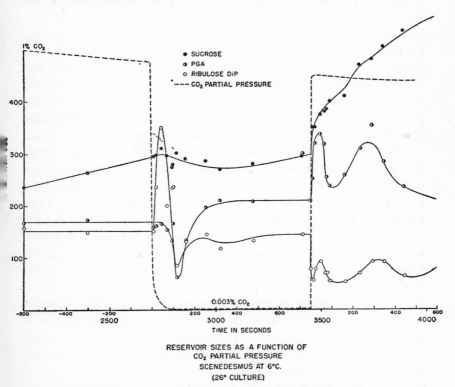

Fig. 12. Reservoir sizes as a function of CO_2 partial pressure, *Scenedesmus* at 6°C.

changes in the steady state found[139] when the CO_2 pressure was reduced from 1% to 0.003% and then increased to 1.0% again are shown in Fig. 12. As would be expected if the carboxylation of RuDP gave PGA, lowering the CO_2 pressure resulted in an increase in RuDP concentration and a decrease in PGA concentration, while raising the CO_2 pressure increased PGA concentration and decreased RuDP concentration. Thus, the carboxylation of RuDP followed by the transformation of the resulting unstable addition product to at least one molecule of PGA seems well substantiated.

An important question regarding the carboxylation reaction is whether the addition product splits to give two molecules of PGA or whether only one molecule of PGA is formed, the other half of the addition product being reduced directly to triose phosphate. The light-dark transient studies discussed earlier showed that on turning off the light, the carboxylation reaction *in vivo* does result in the formation of two molecules of PGA per carboxylation. Moreover, the isolated enzyme, carboxydismutase, has been found to give only PGA as a product when given ribulose diphosphate and CO_2 as the substrate. However, there remains the possibility that as long as the light remains on, the *in vivo* reaction might lead to direct reduction.

An indication of the possible mechanism of the reaction was sought in close examination of the initial transients in the concentrations of PGA, RuDP, and related compounds that accompanied restoration of CO_2 to 1% after the CO_2 pressure had been 0.003%. A lower limit for the maximum rates of change would be obtained from the first point (5 sec., 6°, Fig. 12). For this 5-second point it is seen that the increase in total carbon in PGA is approximately $\frac{3}{5}$ the decrease in total carbon of RuDP, or in other words, there is an increase of only one mole of PGA for a decrease of one mole in RuDP. This might suggest that about half of the expected PGA was either immediately reduced or was not formed. A mechanism for the latter possibility is shown in the second reaction (L) on the following page.

Reaction (D) is the reaction indicated by the light-dark transient studies and by the studies of carboxydismutase, *in vitro*. Reaction (L) is a reaction which might occur only in the light, predominating at higher concentrations of reducing agent (photochemically produced)

$$CH_2O\circledP \quad CH_2O\circledP$$
$$O=\overset{+}{C}-C-OH \quad -O_2C-\overset{}{C}-OH$$
$$| \quad | $$
$$O^- \quad C-OH \quad\quad C=O$$
$$| \quad\quad\quad\quad |$$
$$CHOH \quad\quad CHOH$$
$$| \quad\quad\quad\quad\quad |$$
$$CH_2O\circledP \quad\quad CH_2O\circledP$$

RuDP (-enol form)
$\circledP = -PO_3H^-$

$\xrightarrow{+OH^-}$ (D) $CH_2-CHOH-CO_2^-$
$\quad\quad\quad\quad\quad\quad\quad |$
$\quad\quad\quad\quad\quad\quad O\circledP$ PGA

$\xrightarrow{+2(H)}$ (L) $CH_2-CHOH-CO_2^- + CH_2-CHOH-C=O$
$\quad\quad\quad\quad\quad |\quad\quad\quad\quad\quad\quad\quad\quad\quad\quad\quad |$
$\quad\quad\quad\quad\quad O\circledP$ PGA $\quad\quad\quad\quad O\circledP$ H
$\quad\quad\quad\quad\quad\quad\quad\quad\quad\quad\quad\quad\quad\quad$ Phosphoglyceraldehyde

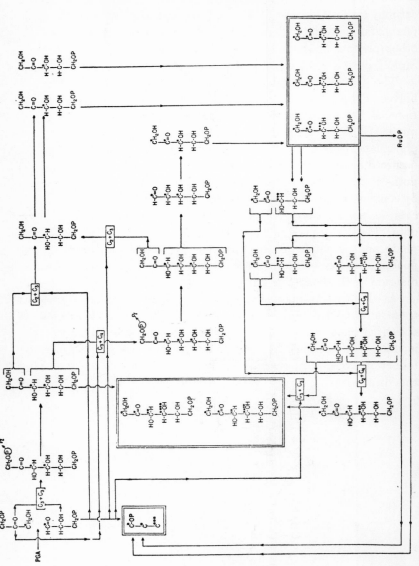

Fig. 13. The redistribution of carbon in sugar arrangements.

in which half of the product should appear at the oxidation level of carbohydrate. The missing carbon does not appear in triose phosphate, but may have been transformed even in this short time to other products, especially sucrose which is seen to increase very rapidly during this 5-second period.

The degradation data of Gibbs and Kandler,[50] in which the two halves of the hexose molecule were found to have different distributions of C^{14} following short periods of photosynthesis with $C^{14}O_2$, might also be interpreted as indicating two different sources of triose phosphate, one of which is not PGA. If only partial equilibration occurred between the triose phosphate molecules from these two hypothetical sources, unequal labeling of the hexose molecule formed by condensation of two triose phosphate molecules could result. However, as was shown earlier, there are other ways of explaining these data. Thus, any process which builds up the pool of ribose-5-phosphate and permits a feedback of the top two carbon atoms of this pool into hexose could provide the unsymmetrical labeling. A detailed diagram of these labeling patterns is shown in Fig. 13.

At this writing it is not possible to decide conclusively between these alternatives, but since reaction (*D*) has been established as occurring under some conditions, while the evidence for reaction (*L*) is still very tenuous, the carboxylation reaction of the carbon-reduction cycle will be written as reaction (*D*) for the remainder of this discussion.

VI

Photosynthetic Carbon-Reduction Cycle

1. FORMULATION

The photosynthetic carbon-reduction cycle, as presently envisioned, is shown in Fig. 14. Also shown are the various enzymes postulated to carry out the several steps.

The two points at which there seems to be a reasonable possibility that the pathway might be different from the one shown are in the splitting of the carboxylation product (discussed in the preceding section) and in the enzymatic mechanism by which sedoheptulose phosphate and ribulose monophosphate are formed, either from fructose-6-phosphate, phosphodihydroxyacetone and phosphoglyceraldehyde, as shown in Fig. 14, or from two molecules of hexose phosphate.

The carbon balance of the cycle is indicated in the following scheme:

$$3C_5 \xrightarrow{3ATP} 3RuDP$$

$$3RuDP + 3CO_2 \longrightarrow 6PGA$$

$$6PGA \xrightarrow[6ATP]{12(H)} 6C_3$$

$$2C_3 \longrightarrow C_6$$

$$C_6 + 2C_3 \longrightarrow C_5 + C_7$$

$$C_7 + C_3 \longrightarrow 2C_5$$

$$\overline{12(H) + 3CO_2 \xrightarrow[12(H)]{9ATP} C_3 + 3H_2O}$$

The net result of one complete turn of the cycle is the conversion of three molecules of CO_2 to triose phosphate by 12 equivalents of reducing agent (hydrogen atoms) and nine molecules of ATP (converted in the process to nine ADP molecules, eight inorganic phosphate molecules, and the phosphate groups of triose phosphate). The triose phosphate may be used in the synthesis of carbohydrates or glycerol. Since the process is cyclic, carbon may be drained off at any other point; for example, PGA may be converted to pyruvate for fatty acid or amino acid synthesis. These and other synthetic processes leading from the carbon-reduction cycle will be considered later on.

2. Enzymes of the carbon-reduction cycle

(a) *Carboxydismutase.* The enzymatic carboxylation of ribulose diphosphate was first reported by Quayle[98] who demonstrated the formation of phosphoglyceric acid, labeled with C^{14} in the carboxyl group only, when ribulose diphosphate and $C^{14}O_2$ were added to a

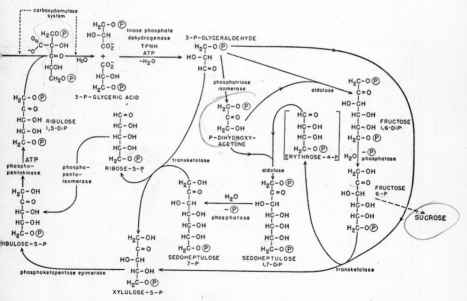

Fig. 14. The photosynthetic carbon-reduction cycle.

cell-free extract obtained from *Chlorella*. This enzyme was named carboxydismutase by these workers who were the first to identify the reaction *in vitro* in terms of both substrates and products. Shortly afterwards, Weissbach[134] reported studies of a soluble extract from spinach leaves which was capable of catalyzing the fixation of CO_2 into PGA in the presence of ribose-5-phosphate. When the presence in these spinach extracts of an enzyme system capable of forming RuDP from R-5-P with ATP was reported by Weissbach[135] it appeared that the spinach extracts used by these workers might also contain an enzyme capable of carboxylating RuDP. Further work with *Chlorella* extracts by Kornberg[78] indicated that the carboxylation of RuDP did not require ATP and did not yield phosphoglyceraldehyde as one of its products. In the meantime three independent studies with purified enzyme preparations from spinach leaves[88,99,132] had established the stoichiometry of the CO_2 fixation reaction *in vitro* as the formation of two molecules of PGA from one molecule of RuDP and one molecule of CO_2 (or bicarbonate ion). Further studies of this enzyme were reported in 1956 by Weissbach[133] and by Jakoby.[71] It was established by Weissbach that the carboxylation reaction with RuDP, which was labeled in the number 1 carbon atom resulted in β carbon-labeled PGA, as would be expected in the mechanism proposed earlier.

(b) *Phosphoglyceryl Kinase*. Although not shown separately in Fig. 14, the reduction of PGA to triose phosphate may require two steps, if its conversion follows a pathway which is the reverse of the glycolytic pathway. The first step is the formation of diphosphoglyceric acid from PGA. The enzyme for this reaction requires ATP as a cofactor. This enzyme has been extracted from viable pea seeds.[7]

(c) *Triose Phosphate Dehydrogenase*. The reduction of diphosphoglyceric acid to triose phosphate may be carried out by a triose phosphate dehydrogenase. The presence of such an enzyme in plants has been reported by Stumpf.[120,121] This enzyme required DPN as a cofactor. Two dehydrogenases which require TPN have been found to occur in green tissues.[3,49] The triose phosphate dehydrogenase found in seeds and in seedlings germinated in the dark requires DPN but when seedlings are exposed to light, a TPN-requiring dehydrogenase appears.[55]

(d) *Triose Phosphate Isomerase.* Triose phosphate isomerase activity has been demonstrated in pea seed extracts.[124]

(e) *Aldolase.* The presence of aldolase in plant tissues has been reported by Stumpf[120,123] and by Hough and Jones[66] who reported the formation of sedoheptulose when aldolase from peas was incubated with dihydroxyacetone phosphate and D-erythrose.

(f) *Phosphatase.* A phosphatase which catalyzes the formation of fructose-6-phosphate from fructose diphosphate was obtained from liver by Gomori[51] and has been highly purified from spinach extracts by Racker.[88] No hydrolysis of several monophosphate esters of hexoses and pentoses could be detected with this purified enzyme. This phosphatase also catalyzes the hydrolysis of sedoheptulose diphosphate.

(g) *Transketolase.* Transketolase has been obtained in crystalline form from yeast extracts[101] and highly purified from liver and spinach.[64] The action of this enzyme is the transfer of a glycolyl group (carbon atoms 1 and 2) from a ketose monophosphate to an aldose phosphate as shown in the following scheme:

$$
\begin{array}{llllll}
1 & CH_2OH & & 1 & CH_2OH & \\
2 & C{=}O & 4\ H{-}C{=}O & 2 & C{=}O & 3\ HC{=}O \\
3\ HO{-}CH & + & (CHOH)n & \longrightarrow & 4\ HO{-}CH & + & (CHOH)m \\
(CHOH)m & & CH_2O\textcircled{P} & & (CHOH)n & CH_2O\textcircled{P} \\
CH_2O\textcircled{P} & & & & CH_2O\textcircled{P} &
\end{array}
$$

$$ m = 0,1,2,3 \qquad n = 0,1,2,3 $$

(h) *Transaldolase.* Transaldolase, reported by Horecker,[63] transfers carbon atoms 1, 2, and 3 of ketose monophosphate to an aldose phosphate as shown in the example, page 60. Although not included in the scheme as written in Fig. 14, it has been suggested that transaldolase plays a part in the sugar rearrangements of the carbon-reduction cycle.[88] Instead of the condensation of dihydroxyacetone

phosphate with erythrose phosphate by aldolase, leading to sedoheptulose diphosphate, the formation of heptose would occur by a
removal and transfer of carbon atoms 1, 2, and 3 of fructose-6-
phosphate to a condensation with erythrose phosphate to produce
sedoheptulose-7-phosphate and glyceraldehyde phosphate. The two
alternative pathways are as follows:

(I)

$$
\begin{array}{ccc}
\text{H}_2\text{CO}\textcircled{P} & \text{H}_2\text{CO}\textcircled{P} & \text{H}_2\text{COH} \\
| & | & | \\
\text{C}=\text{O} & \text{C}=\text{O} & \text{C}=\text{O} \\
| & | & | \\
\text{H}_2\text{COH} & \text{HOCH} & \text{HOCH} \\
& \xrightarrow{\text{aldolase}} \text{HCOH} \xrightarrow[\text{phosphatase}]{\text{H}_2\text{O}} & \text{HCOH} + \text{HO}\textcircled{P} \\
+ & | & | \\
\text{HC}=\text{O} & \text{HCOH} & \text{HCOH} \\
| & | & | \\
\text{HCOH} & \text{HCOH} & \text{HCOH} \\
| & | & | \\
\text{HCOH} & \text{H}_2\text{CO}\textcircled{P} & \text{H}_2\text{CO}\textcircled{P} \\
| & & \\
\text{H}_2\text{CO}\textcircled{P} & &
\end{array}
$$

(II)

$$
\begin{array}{cccc}
\text{H}_2\text{CO}\textcircled{P} & \text{H}_2\text{CO}\textcircled{P} & \text{H}_2\text{COH} & \text{H}_2\text{COH} \\
| & | & | & | \\
\text{HC}=\text{O} & \text{C}=\text{O} & \text{C}=\text{O} & \text{C}=\text{O} \\
| & | & | & | \\
\text{H}_2\text{COH} & \text{HOCH} & \text{HOCH} & \text{HOCH} \\
& \xrightarrow{\text{aldolase}} \text{HCOH} \xrightarrow[\text{phosphatase}]{\text{H}_2\text{O}} \text{HCOH} \xrightarrow{\text{transaldolase}} \text{HCOH} + \text{HC}=\text{O} \\
+ & | & | & | \quad\quad | \\
& \text{HCOH} & \text{HCOH} & \text{HCOH} \quad \text{HCOH} \\
\text{HC}=\text{O} & \text{H}_2\text{CO}\textcircled{P} & \text{[H}_2\text{CO}\textcircled{P} \quad \text{HC}=\text{O} & \text{HCOH} \quad \text{H}_2\text{CO}\textcircled{P} \\
| & & + \quad\quad | & | \\
\text{HCOH} & & \text{HCOH} & \text{H}_2\text{CO}\textcircled{P} \\
| & & \text{HO}\textcircled{P}] \quad | & \\
\text{H}_2\text{CO}\textcircled{P} & & \text{HCOH} & \\
& & | & \\
& & \text{H}_2\text{CO}\textcircled{P} &
\end{array}
$$

The basic similarity of the two processes is readily apparent. The
same rearrangement of carbon chains is accomplished. The processes
are similar energetically, since each involves the hydrolysis of a
phosphate ester on the number 1 carbon atoms. However, it should
be noted that the transaldolase sequence (II) involves an extra enzymatic step. Therefore, it might be argued that on the basis of

economy of motion, process (I) is slightly more probable; but no positive choice can be made at this time.

(i) *Phosphoriboseisomerase.* Phosphoriboseisomerase has been obtained from yeast preparations,[65] alfalfa,[8] and spinach.[67] This enzyme brings about the interconversion of ribose-5-phosphate and ribulose-5-phosphate, the equilibrium mixture being 70% ribose-5-phosphate and 30% ribulose-5-phosphate.

(j) *Ribulose Phosphate-Xylulose Phosphate Isomerase* (*Phosphoketopentose epimerase*). Ribulose phosphate-xylulose phosphate isomerase was reported from yeast by Srere,[114] and from *Lactobacillus pentosus* by Stumpf[122] who named it phosphoketopentose epimerase. This enzyme brings about the interconversion of ribulose-5-phosphate and xylulose-5-phosphate, and isomerization at the number 3 carbon atom. Stumpf found the equilibrium ratio of ribulose-5-phosphate to xylulose-5-phosphate to be about 1.2.

(k) *Phosphoribulokinase.* Phosphoribulokinase has been purified from spinach leaf extract by Hurwitz.[67] This enzyme is responsible for the formation of ribulose diphosphate from ribulose-5-phosphate and ATP.

$$\text{Ru-5-P} + \text{ATP} \xrightarrow{\text{phosphoribulokinase}} \text{RuDP} + \text{ADP}$$

In the presence of excess ATP, Ru-5-P is completely converted to RuDP.

3. ENERGETICS

From the above discussion of the enzymes of the carbon-reduction cycle it can be seen that energy is supplied to the cycle in the form of chemical energy stored in the chemical bonds of certain cofactors. As the cycle is written, the total supply of such energy, for each complete turn of the cycle, comes from two molecules of reduced coenzyme II (TPNH) and three molecules of ATP.

Since the condition of photosynthesis in an active green plant is a condition of dynamic steady state, rather than an equilibrium, there is a certain excess of energy supplied to the cycle over that stored in the form of reduced carbon compounds which are the end products of the operation of the cycle. This excess of free energy is required to keep the cycle turning with a rapid net flow of material from one intermediate compound to the next in the forward direction.

The calculations which follow show that the excess free energy, which will be called E, for each carbon atom reduced, is distributed among various reactions of the carbon-reduction cycle in such a way as to keep the cycle running smoothly and rapidly in the forward direction, without vanishingly small concentrations of any of the postulated intermediates. The assumptions and results involved in these calculations will be summarized.*

1. The calculations of reaction energies of enzymatic steps from glucose to pyruvic acid are based on the published calculations of Burton and Wilson[32] and of Burton and Krebs.[31]

2. Following their system, free energies were first calculated for all compounds from glucose to pyruvate at concentrations of $10^{-2}M$ aq., $pH = 7.0$, $O_2 = 0.21$ atm., $CO_2 = 0.05$ atm.

3. After these calculations gave free energy values for glucose and fructose, the free energies of these hexoses in their straight-chain form were calculated, using published data that 0.024% of glucose in solution is in straight-chain form and a corresponding value of 0.28% for fructose which was estimated. These straight-chain free energy values plus free energy values for glyceraldehyde, dihydroxyacetone, and glycerol, all in solution, were used in setting up an empirical calculation of the free energies of ribose, ribulose, sedoheptulose, and erythrose.

4. The ring stabilization of sedoheptulose was assumed to be the same as that of fructose; the ring stabilization of ribose was calculated from published data concerning the amount of straight-chain form in solution.

---

* The following abbreviating symbols are used: E4P, erythrose-4-phosphate; DHAP, dihydroxyacetone phosphate; SDP, sedoheptulose diphosphate; GA13P, glyceraldehyde-3-phosphate; FDP, fructose diphosphate; S7P, sedoheptulose-7-phosphate; F6P, fructose-6-phosphate; RuDP, ribulose diphosphate; Ru5P, ribulose-5-phosphate; ATP, adenosine triphosphate; ADP, adenosine diphosphate; Ri5P, ribose-5-phosphate; TPNH, reduced triphosphopyridine nucleotide; TPN, triphosphonucleotide; G6P, glucose-6-phosphate; Xu5P, xylulose-5-phosphate.

5. The free energies of formation of erythrose-4-phosphate, sedoheptulose-7-phosphate, and ribose-5-phosphate from their respective free sugars and inorganic phosphate were all assumed to be the same.

6. The free energy of hydrolysis of ATP to ADP and inorganic phosphate, at $1M$ concentrations and at $pH = 7$, was taken as $\Delta F = -8.1$ kcal. For $10^{-2}M$ concentrations this gives $\Delta F' = -10.8$ kcal.[30]

7. Other reactions were assumed to have the same energies as analogous reactions. These included:

$$E4P^{-2} + DHAP^{-2} \longrightarrow SDP^{-4}$$

assumed same as

$$GA13P^{-2} + DHAP^{-2} \longrightarrow FDP^{-4}$$

$$SDP^{-4} + H_2O \longrightarrow HPO_4^{-2} + S7P^{-2}$$

assumed same as

$$FDP^{-2} + H_2O \longrightarrow HPO_4^{-2} + F6P^{-2}$$

The free energies of formation of all intermediates in the carbon-reduction cycle are given in Table III. In this table, ΔF values are

Table III. Free Energies of Formation of Intermediates in the Carbon-Reduction Cycle

Compound	ΔF $10^{-2}M$ aq.	Conc. in CO_2 red. system at x $10^{-2}M$	$\Delta F'$ at PS conc.
PGA	℗ −157.2	1.63	℗ −156.9
GA13P	℗ −102.7	0.05 (est.)	℗ −104.5
DHAP	℗ −104.5	0.11 (est.)	℗ −105.8
FDP	2℗ −210.0	0.004	2℗ −213.5
F6P	℗ −216.5	0.12	℗ −217.8
G6P	℗ −217.0	0.33	℗ −217.7
E4P	℗ −139.1	0.001 (est.)	℗ −143.2
SDP	2℗ −246.6	0.006	2℗ −249.6
S7P	℗ −252.9	0.25	℗ −253.8
Ri5P	℗ −177.2	0.10 (est.)	℗ −178.6
Ru5P	℗ −177.6	0.07 (est.)	℗ −178.2
Xu5P	℗ −176.5	0.03 (est.)	℗ −178.7
RuDP	2℗ −170.1	0.51	2℗ −170.6
HCO_3^-	−142.9	0.187	−143.9

calculated both for dissolved reductants at $10^{-2}M$ aq. and for the actual concentrations measured by kinetic studies during photosynthesis (see Table II), with the arbitrary assumption that the space actually occupied by the carbon-reduction system is 0.1 the wet packed volume of the algae.

The free energies of the various steps in the carbon-reduction cycle follow:

(1)* $HCO_3^- + RuDP^{-4} \longrightarrow 2PGA^{-3} + H^+$ $\Delta F' = -8.9$ kcal.

(2) $Ru5P^{-2} + ATP^{-4}$
      $\longrightarrow RuDP^{-4} + ADP^{-3} + H^+$ $\Delta F' = -3.2$

(3) $Ri5P^{-2} \longrightarrow Ru5P^{-2}$ $\Delta F' = +0.4**$

(4) $S7P^{-2} + GA13P^{-2} \longrightarrow Ri5P^{-2} + Xu5P^{-2}$ $\Delta F' = +1.0$

(5) $SDP^{-4} + H_2O \longrightarrow S7P^{-2} + HPO_4^{-2}$ $\Delta F' = -4.1$

(6) $E4P^{-2} + DHAP^{-2} \longrightarrow SDP^{-4}$ $\Delta F' = -0.6$

(7) $F6P^{-2} + GA13P^{-2} \longrightarrow Xu5P^{-2} + E4P^{-2}$ $\Delta F' = +0.4$

(8) $FDP^{-4} + H_2O \longrightarrow F6P^{-2} + HPO_4^{-2}$ $\Delta F' = -4.3$

(9) $GA13P^{-2} + DHAP^{-2} \longrightarrow FDP^{-4}$ $\Delta F' = -3.2$

(10) $GA13P^{-2} \longrightarrow DHAP^{-2}$ $\Delta F' = -1.3$

(11) $PGA^{-3} + ATP^{-4} + TPNH + H^+ \longrightarrow$
      $GA13P^{-2} + TPN^+ + ADP^{-3} + HPO_4^{-2}$ $\Delta F' = -1.2$

(12) $Xu5P^{-2} \longrightarrow Ru5P^{-2}$ $\Delta F' = +0.5$

* Reaction (1) has been formulated in two stages, as shown on page 53, reaction (*D*). The standard free energy in the first stage may be positive placing the keto acid in the position of a high energy intermediate between the initial reactants and final products as shown in reaction (1). One may, therefore, expect small concentrations of the keto acid to be found in any steady-state experiment. This has, indeed, proved to be the case in experiments by V. Moses in our laboratory, in which approximately 5% of the diphosphate is keto acid diphosphate in a 3-minute photosynthetic experiment with *Chlorella*.

** Of course, the true free energy change (corrected) for activities of all reactants and products *must be negative for each step* in the forward direction in a sequence of reactions at steady state. The fact that apparent positive free energy changes are obtained in some of the steps shown here stems from the fact that the levels of some of the reactants, such as ATP, ADP, TPNH and TPN^+, etc. may be different from the assumed values, or from inaccuracies in the measurement of the concentrations of some of the less stable intermediates, or both.

For each complete turn of the carbon-reduction cycle, three molecules of CO_2 are taken up, six molecules of PGA produced, and the various steps in the cycle take place the number of times indicated below. The free energy change of each step per cycle can therefore be calculated.

Step No.	$\Delta F'$	No. of times N	$N\Delta F'$
1	−8.9	3	−26.7
2	−3.2	3	−9.6
3	+0.4	1	+0.4
4	+1.0	1	+1.0
5	−4.1	1	−4.1
6	−0.6	1	−0.6
7	+0.4	1	+0.4
8	−4.3	$1\frac{1}{2}$ $(1 + \frac{1}{2}*)$	−6.5
9	−3.2	$1\frac{1}{2}$ $(1 + \frac{1}{2}*)$	−4.8
10	−1.3	$2\frac{1}{2}$ $(1 + \frac{1}{2}*)$	−3.3
11	−1.2	6	−7.2
12	+0.5	2	+1.0
		Total:	−60.0

* These amounts needed for noncyclic formations of end product, $3[CH_2O]$.

These reactions bring the three carbon atoms to the energy level of F6P. To bring them to the energy level of glucose two more steps are needed:

(13) $\qquad F6P^{-2} \longrightarrow G6P^{-2} \qquad \Delta F' = +0.1$

(14) $\qquad G6P^{-2} + H_2O \longrightarrow glucose + HPO_4^{-2} \quad \Delta F' = -4.4$

Each of these steps occurs one-half time per turn of the cycle (three carbon atoms) so to −60.0 must be added

$$\tfrac{1}{2}(-4.4 + 0.1) = -2.2$$

to give a total of 62.2 kcal. For each HCO_3^- molecule reduced this is $E = -62.2/3 = -20.7$ kcal. This represents the excess of energy supplied to the carbon-reduction cycle over that stored in the form of reduced carbon.

The energy stored for the reduction of one HCO_3^- molecule to glucose is given by:

(15) $HCO_3^- + H^+ \longrightarrow [CH_2O] + O_2$ $\Delta F' = +115.6$ kcal.

The energy supplied to the cycle for each HCO_3^- reduced may be calculated as that expended by the hydrolysis of three molecules of ATP and the oxidation of two molecules of TPNH.

The oxidation of TPNH by O_2 is given by the sum of:

(16) $TPNH \longrightarrow TPN^+ + H^+ + 2e^-$ $\Delta F = -\ 14.9$

(17) $\frac{1}{2}O_2 + 2e^- + 2H^+ \longrightarrow H_2O$ $\Delta F = -\ 36.7$

which is

(18) $TPNH + \frac{1}{2}O_2 + H^+ \longrightarrow H_2O + TPN^+$ $\Delta F = -\ 51.6$

The sum of the oxidation of 2TPNH is $2(-51.6)$ $\Delta F = -103.2$
and hydrolysis of 3(ATP) $3(-10.8)$. . . . . $\Delta F = -\ 32.4$

which is. . . . . $\Delta F = -135.6$

The energy given out by twice reaction (18) plus the hydrolysis of three ATP molecules differs from the energy stored in reaction (15) by $-135.6 + 115.6 = -20.0$ kcal. This corresponds to E, the energy expended in keeping the cycle running at a dynamic steady state. At equilibrium, E would be zero.

VII

Pathway of Carbon into Carbohydrates

---

1. SUCROSE

As shown in the discussion of the carbon-reduction cycle, each two turns of the cycle can result in the reduction of six molecules of carbon dioxide and the formation of a molecule of hexose phosphate. This hexose phosphate may be used in the synthesis of sucrose or other polysaccharides.

The sucrose phosphorylase enzyme from *Pseudomonas saccharophila* was known to catalyze the reactions

sucrose $+ H_3PO_4 \rightleftarrows \alpha$-$D$-glucose-1-phosphate $+ D$-fructose,

Hassid, Doudoroff, and Barker[57] having isolated sucrose synthesized by this enzyme. It appeared, however, that this was not the mechanism by which sucrose is synthesized in the green plant. It was not possible to show the presence of this enzyme in higher plants. It was found that when *Chlorella* were allowed to photosynthesize in radioactive carbon dioxide, sucrose was the first free sugar to be formed. This was interpreted to mean that in sucrose synthesis in higher plants, only phosphorylated derivatives of sugars were involved, probably yielding a sucrose phosphate as the first sucrose-containing product. Putman,[97] working with leaf punches, obtained evidence for the formation of a phosphorylated sucrose derivative in sucrose synthesis.

A study of the phosphorylated products of short-term photosynthesis in $C^{14}O_2$ led to the discovery of a sucrose phosphate.[27] The "hexose monophosphates" produced during photosynthesis in $C^{14}O_2$ were treated with an invertase-free phosphatase preparation and subjected to paper chromatography. While in most cases there were only minute traces of sucrose formed by this treatment, in sugar beet (5 minutes in $C^{14}O_2$) there was an appreciable quantity. It was identified by co-chromatography, and enzymatic hydrolysis to glucose and fructose.

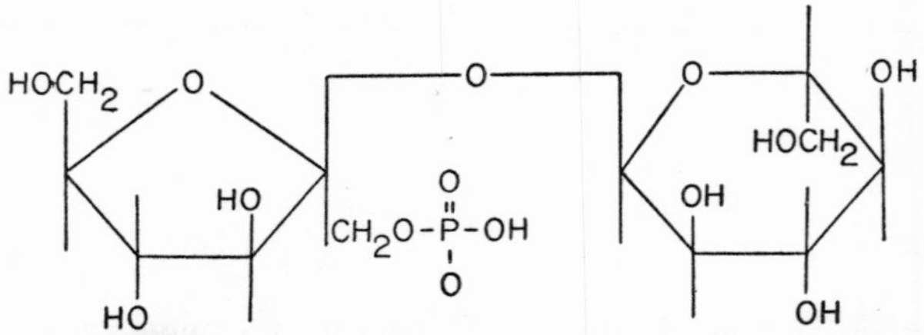

Fig. 15. Proposed structure for sucrose phosphate.

When this "hexose monophosphate" sample was subjected to chromatography in *t*-butanol/picric acid/water, radioactive areas corresponding to glucose-6-phosphate, fructose-6-phosphate, sedoheptulose and mannose phosphates, and sucrose phosphate were obtained. The sucrose phosphate gave sucrose on phosphatase treatment, and on acid hydrolysis, glucose and fructose phosphate were produced. The latter did not co-chromatograph with fructose-6-phosphate.

It was proposed that sucrose phosphate in sugar beet leaves had the probable structure shown in Fig. 15.

It appeared that in sucrose synthesis in green plants there are two possible mechanisms. Glucose-1-phosphate might react with fructose-1-phosphate to give sucrose phosphate, which would be dephosphorylated to sucrose. Alternatively, sucrose phosphate synthesis might be envisaged to occur through uridine diphosphate glucose[28] which becomes labeled shortly before sucrose in kinetic experiments with $C^{14}O_2$.[21] The uridine diphosphate glucose may be formed from glucose-1-phosphate by a series of reactions analogous to those proposed by A. Kornberg.[77] These alternative schemes are summarized in Fig. 16.

Leloir and Cardini[81] have isolated from wheat germ what appears to be two systems, one which catalyzes the reaction of fructose plus UDPG to give sucrose plus UDP and the other which catalyzes the reaction UDPG plus fructose-6-phosphate to give sucrose phosphate plus UDP. Burma and Mortimer[29] have reported that with excised

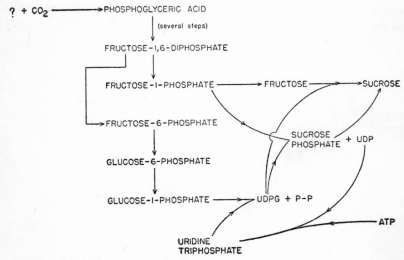

Fig. 16. Proposed mechanism for formation of sucrose with UDPG.

sugar beet leaves and leaf homogenates radioactive UDPG and sucrose were formed when radioactive glucose-1-phosphate, fructose-6-phosphate, and UTP were added. He proposes a mechanism identical to that postulated by Buchanan[28] except in his choice of fructose-6-phosphate as the precursor instead of fructose-1-phosphate.

The requirement of ATP in this mechanism of sucrose synthesis is believed to result in an acceleration of this reaction in the light (during photosynthesis) so that in this sense this reaction is part of the pathway of carbon in photosynthesis.

While not much is known about the formation of other polysaccharides during photosynthesis, it may be postulated that mechanisms similar to that postulated for the formation of sucrose may account for the rapid formation of polysaccharides labeled with C^{14} which has been observed to occur during many experiments in which plants have been allowed to photosynthesize with $C^{14}O_2$ for relatively short periods. On the usual two-dimensional chromatogram, developed as described earlier, these compounds form what appears to be a homologous series extending from the origin to sucrose. The compound of this series closest to sucrose has been hydrolyzed and found to contain only glucose.

VIII

Fat Synthesis

---

1. FATTY ACIDS

During photosynthesis with $C^{14}O_2$ with *Scenedesmus* as much as 30% of the radiocarbon incorporated in 5 minutes has been found in lipid materials. Since this incorporation of radiocarbon is greatly in excess of the rate of dark respiration, it may be taken as an indication of the stimulation of fat production in the light. In view of the greater number of equivalents of reducing agents required to reduce CO_2 to fats as compared to the number required to form carbohydrate, it is not surprising that rapid fat synthesis requires reducing agents derived from the light.

When C^{14}-labeled acetate was added to *Chlorella* in the light and in the dark, it was found that light greatly stimulated the incorporation of the acetate into radioactive lipids. It seems reasonable to suppose that CO_2, incorporated into PGA via the carbon-reduction cycle finds its way into fatty acids via PGA, pyruvic acid, and an active acetyl group, such as acetyl coenzyme A.

Another route by which intermediates of the carbon-reduction cycle may be converted to fatty acids is the possible conversion of two carbon units, derived from sugar phosphates, into acetate, acetyl phosphate, or acetyl CoA. For example, if ribulose-5-phosphate were split to glyceraldehyde phosphate and glycolaldehyde, the later compound could rearrange to give acetyl phosphate.

71

$$
\begin{array}{ccc}
\text{H}_2\text{COH} & & \text{H}_2\text{COH} \\
| & & | \\
\text{C}{=}\text{O} & \longrightarrow & \text{HC}{=}\text{O} \\
| & & \\
\text{HCOH} & & + \\
| & & \\
\text{HCOH} & & \text{HC}{=}\text{O} \\
| & & | \\
\text{H}_2\text{CO}\circledP & & \text{HCOH} \\
& & | \\
& & \text{H}_2\text{CO}\circledP
\end{array}
$$

$$
\begin{array}{c}
\text{H}_2\text{COH} \\
| \\
\text{HC}{=}\text{O}
\end{array}
\xrightarrow[-\text{H}_2\text{O}\,+\,\text{HOPO}_3\text{H}^-]{}
\begin{array}{c}
\text{CH}_3 \\
| \\
\text{COPO}_3\text{H}^- \\
\| \\
\text{O}
\end{array}
$$

2. GLYCEROL

While no direct evidence has been obtained as yet, it seems likely that glycerol phosphate may be formed at a rapid rate from triose phosphate in the light by reduction owing to reduced cofactors formed from the photolysis of water.*

* The presence of relatively large amounts of α,α'-diglycerophosphate in algae and some higher plants has recently been reported. Maruo, B. and Benson, A. A.: "α,α'-Diglycerophate in Plants," *J. Am. Chem. Soc.*, **79**, 4564-4565 (1957).

IX

Amino Acids

A number of labeled amino acids are formed at a rapid rate in the light when the plants are exposed to radioactive CO_2. Alanine, labeled very quickly, is probably formed by transamination from pyruvic acid, while serine is formed by transamination of hydroxypyruvic acid. Glycine may be formed from glyoxylic acid which in turn may arise from the glycolyl fragment which is carried by transketolase in the sugar rearrangement reactions. It may be noted that the occurrence of conditions leading to the formation of large amounts of labeled glycolic acid (such as low CO_2 pressure) often results in the simultaneous formation of increased amounts of glycine.

The other amino acids found to be labeled significantly after short periods of photosynthesis are aspartic acid and glutamic acid. The aspartic acid formation is no doubt associated with the rapid labeling of malic acid which is frequently observed. Malic acid is labeled by a carboxylation reaction in which carbon dioxide undergoes a reductive addition to pyruvic acid. Since the pyruvic acid is derived from PGA, the resulting label of the malic and aspartic acids is $\overset{*}{\underset{*}{C}}OOH—\overset{*}{C}H_2—\overset{*}{C}HOH—\overset{*}{C}OOH$, the actual proportions depending on the label of the PGA from which it is derived. Under nonsteady state conditions the amount of C_3-C_1 carboxylation may be very large. The formation of labeled glutamic acid parallels the incorporation of C^{14} into citric, α-ketoglutaric, and succinic acids. Like these carboxylic acids, glutamic acid becomes labeled very rapidly when plants

73

which have been permitted to incorporate $C^{14}O_2$ in the light (until intermediates of the carbon cycle are well labeled) are then placed in the dark. This accelerated formation is believed to be due to a combination of a release from light inhibition of pyruvic acid oxidation and a transient change of pool sizes upon darkening. However, C_2 compounds, including active acetate, glyoxylate and glycolate, may be formed directly from sugar phosphates, presumably by reactions analogous to the transketolase reaction. From these compounds there may be synthesized either fatty acids (as suggested in the last section) or malic and α-ketoglutaric acids* by a pathway not subject to the postulated inhibition by light of pyruvic acid oxidation.

* A route from C_2 compounds to α-ketoglutarate has recently been described by H. L. Kornberg and H. A. Krebs ["Synthesis of Cell Constituents from C_2-Units by a Modified Tricarboxylic Acid Cycle," *Nature*, **179**, 988-991 (1957)].

X

Metabolic Inhibitors

---

1. General inhibitors

It has long been known that a good many general cell poisons have a marked effect on overall photosynthesis. Such poisons as mercuric ion, hydroxylamine, cyanide, and azide are potent inhibitors of photosynthesis as well as other cellular processes. An early attempt to evaluate or determine the point of selective inhibition by cyanide and by hydroxylamine using the radiocarbon fixation pattern techniques was reported in 1951.[33] It seemed clear from these results that both inhibitors were affecting a number of steps and each to a different degree. This work, particularly with cyanide, was resumed recently in our laboratory under the stimulus of some indications that, under suitable conditions, cyanide might inhibit photosynthesis slightly more than respiratory processes[46,47] and that some form of ATP generation might not be cyanide sensitive.[73] In these experiments[74] use was made of the assumption that injection of a relatively high concentration of inhibitor in the medium would result in a gradient of inhibitions over the following time, as the inhibitor concentration is gradually increased within the cell. A typical experiment of this sort involved a preliminary period of photosynthesis with $C^{14}O_2$ of the order of 10 seconds, followed by the injection of enough cyanide to bring the overall concentration up to approximately 0.02 molar, followed by a further light period of the order of 10 or 20 seconds, after which the reaction was stopped in the usual way with alcohol.

The most pronounced difference that was observed in the chromatograms in such an experiment was a reduction in the amount of phosphoglyceric acid to be seen (compared with the 10 seconds photosynthesis control) and an increase in the amount of radioactivity to be found in the diphosphate area. An examination of this diphosphate area using phosphatase to hydrolyze the phosphate esters produced two new radioactive compounds not seen in the absence of cyanide. These appear to be related as gluconic acid is related to gluconolactone. Further work with this acid established its constitution as hamamelonic acid.[99] This appeared to be related to the keto acid which had been proposed as an intermediate in the carboxylation of ribulose diphosphate and found present to a very small extent in the diphosphate areas.[90] However, a simple direct addition reaction of cyanide on ribulose diphosphate leading to hamamelonic acid diphosphate has been demonstrated.[111] This suggests that at least part, if not all, of the hamamelonic acid diphosphate appearing in the above described photosynthetic experiment has its origin in a nonenzymatic cyanohydrin formation on the ribulose diphosphate present in the cell at the time of the cyanide addition, and that the increase in the amount of this material induced by this succeeding illumination is the result of the conversion of the initially formed phosphoglyceric acid into more ribulose diphosphate. Further degradation experiments are under way to determine the possibility that some of this hamamelonic acid may arise by reduction of the intermediate keto acids.

2. Specific inhibitors

A number of attempts have been made to use specific metabolic inhibitors in order to define further the routes leading from the photosynthetic cycle into a variety of other metabolically synthesized plant materials. Some of the early work in which a wide variety of biologically active compounds were tested for their effects on the fixation of radiocarbon dioxide by algae, both in light and in dark, were reported by Havinga.[58] In this work the primary observation was that of total radiocarbon fixation with only an occasional examination of the fixation pattern by chromatography. While some effects were noticed, no outstanding unequivocal results different from the normal patterns were observed. More recently, a rather specific antimetabolic effect on the carbon dioxide fixation pattern of algae has been observed. The drug which was first observed to produce this effect was azaserine.[10] Similar effects have since been observed as the result of treatment with diazo-oxonorleucine.[128]

Table IV. THE EFFECT OF AZASERINE ON *Scenedesmus*

	Control I	Azaserine I (4 mg.)	Control II	Azaserine II (1 mg.)
Determination on aluminum disc (counts/min.)				
Total fixation.......	22×10^6	27×10^6	29.2×10^6	33×10^6
80% ethanol extract.	45.5%	47%	47.3%	47.3%
20% ethanol extract.	5.9%	7.5%	7.5%	8.5%
Determination on paper (counts/min. equal total radioactivity placed on each paper)				
Glutamine.........	332	1,192	390	1,312
Glutamic acid......	2,066	1,227	2,632	1,139
Aspartic acid.......	4,436	989	7,020	762
Serine.............	1,839	849	2,411	990
Alanine............	1,166	272	2,000	314
Glycine............ Threonine.........	} 400	574	1,045	908
Tyrosine...........	261	171	444	295
Valine.............	1,051	787	1,468	1,053
Sucrose............	923×9.5^a	$2,380 \times 9.5$	937	2,072
Malic acid.........	$3,922 \times 9.5$	$5,814 \times 9.5$	$2,691 \times 9.5$	$4,263 \times 9.5$
Citric acid.........	466×9.5	$1,118 \times 9.5$	145×9.5	400×9.5
α-Ketoglutaric acid..	40	200	270	1,054
Fumaric acid.......	269	108	381	344
Succinic acid.......	1,117	1,689	822	922
Glyceric acid.......	576	966	1,349	845
Glycolic acid.......	200	3,182	240	880
Lipids.............	$1,650 \times 9.5$	$1,259 \times 9.5$	$2,540 \times 9.5$	$1,923 \times 9.5$
Phospholipids.......	$1,229 \times 9.5$	$1,071 \times 9.5$	$1,350 \times 9.5$	853×9.5
Area X...........	$1,001 \times 9.5$	751×9.5	621×9.5	538×9.5
Sugar phosphates, PGA and origin...	$14,040 \times 9.5$	$16,379 \times 9.5$	$15,071 \times 9.5$	$14,424 \times 9.5$

[a] The factor 9.5 was used whenever the radioactivity was counted through aluminum foil.

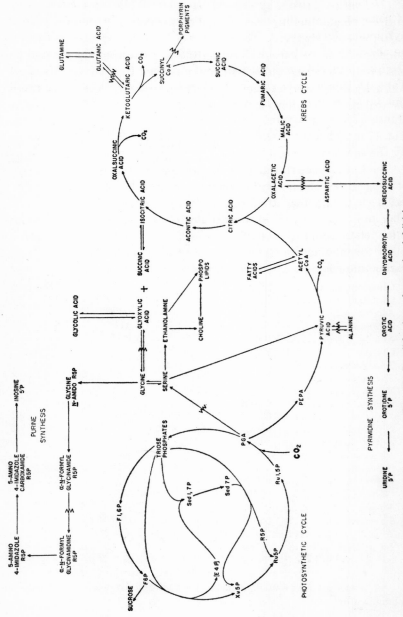

Fig. 17. Possible sites of azaserine inhibition.

The initial observations implicated azaserine as a specific inhibitor of some stages in the metabolic pathway leading to purine and/or pyrimidine synthesis.[56,82] The observations of the effects of azaserine on the path of carbon in photosynthesis by *Scenedesmus* has led to the recognition of a more general, but still specific inhibitory function. Table IV summarizes a typical experiment. The changes apparent in this table are very simply interpreted in terms of a general block of transamination reactions. The various relationships are illustrated in Fig. 17 in which the possible sites of azaserine inhibition are indicated by the saw-tooth lines.

Such studies as this give us considerable further information concerning the secondary and ultimate fate of carbon, initially incorporated via the photosynthetic cycle. It is to be expected that they will play an important part in the ultimate elucidation of all the complex inter-relationships of biosynthesis which make it possible for the green plant to manufacture all of its constituent chemical compounds from carbon dioxide.

XI

Hydrogen Transfer System

While the principal purpose of this monograph has been a discussion of the carbon-reduction pathways in photosynthesis and has now been completed, it seems worthwhile to consider very briefly some other aspects of photosynthesis. These are the directions in which one might search for a better understanding of the principal energy conversion reactions of photosynthesis mentioned in the introduction as

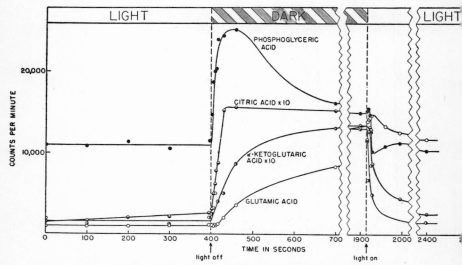

Fig. 18. Light-dark changes in concentrations of PGA, citric acid, and glutamic acid.

reaction (2a) and the ways in which carbon studies herein described might provide some clue to the mechanism of these conversions. Clearly there must be a junction between the products of the initial quantum conversion as written in (2a) and their utilization for carbon reduction as written in (2c). One may, therefore, expect that suitable studies of the behavior of carbon dioxide during the course of its reduction under a sufficiently widely varied set of conditions might give some information about the nature and origin of the reducing agents required which must have their ultimate source in the photochemical act itself. An important experimental operation of this type is depicted in Fig. 18. Here it may be seen that the light in some way prevents the flow of radiocarbon from compounds of the photosynthetic cycle (phosphoglyceric acid) to the compounds of the tricarboxylic cycle or Krebs cycle (citric acid-glutamic acid). This could not reasonably be interpreted in terms of macroscopic substrate concentration changes because the changes in rate of conversion were much greater than the observed change in substrate concentration. Therefore, one must conclude that the light affects the condition of some catalytic substance which may act as a valve between the two cycles. This type of mechanism is shown diagrammatically in Fig. 19 in which the dotted line corresponds to that valve.

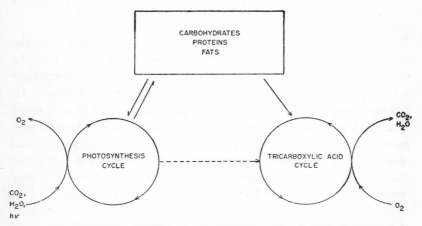

Fig. 19. Schematic diagram of relation between photosynthesis and respiration.

The most direct route from phosphoglyceric acid into the Krebs cycle compounds is via pyruvic acid to acetyl coenzyme A which can then condense with oxalacetic acid to give citric acid. A cofactor for the conversion of pyruvic acid to carbon dioxide and acetyl CoA by pyruvic oxidase is lipoic acid which functions at very low concentrations and which appears to be susceptible to more or less direct transformation as a result of the photochemical process.[11,26,52,54,117] In order to carry the acetyl group from pyruvic acid to CoA, lipoic acid must be present in an oxidized form as shown:

Photosynthetic cycle

$$CH_3 \cdot CO \cdot CO_2H + H_2C \overset{CH_2}{\diagdown} CH \cdot [CH_2]_4 \cdot COX \quad \alpha\text{-Lipoic acid}$$

$$S \text{——} S \qquad R$$

$$(H_2O)[h\nu] \uparrow \downarrow \quad [O] \text{ (DPN)}$$

$$AcS \cdot CoA + H_2C \overset{CH_2}{\diagdown} CHR \overset{CoA \cdot SH}{\longleftarrow} H_2C \overset{CH_2}{\diagdown} CHR + CO_2$$

$$HS \quad SH \qquad\qquad AcS \quad SH$$

$$CO \cdot CO_2H \qquad\qquad\qquad \text{"Active acetyl"}$$
$$CH_2 \cdot CO_2H$$

Citric acid ——————————→ Tricarboxylic acid cycle

If the light, by means of reducing agents it generates, increases the steady-state ratio reduced to oxidized lipoic acid, it is clear that the rate of passage of acetyl through this system from phosphoglyceric acid to citric acid will be reduced. While there may be other catalytic factors susceptible to control by the light which could in turn effect this valving action, this one seems most closely and obviously suggested by the direct relation of phosphoglyceric acid and citric acid shown in Fig. 18. This evidence for the reduction of lipoic acid in the light, and the fact that the oxidation potential of lipoic acid is very nearly identical with pyridine nucleotide[108] believed to be required for reduction of phosphoglyceric acid in the CO_2 reduction cycle, suggest the possible role of lipoic acid as an electron carrier. How many chemical steps may lie between the photochemical excitation of chlorophyll to produce reducing electrons and the reduction of lipoic acid is not known, but the ease of the noncatalyzed reduction suggests there may be very few, if any. A study of the ability of lipoic acid to accept electrons from the photochemical source as it exists in the chloroplast shows it to be highly efficient compared to other electron acceptors which have been used, such as quinone and ferric ion in various forms.[24]

XII

Quantum Conversion Process

This last reaction, first developed by Hill, is the one in which the photochemical apparatus is removed from the green plants in the form of chloroplasts or chloroplast fragments which are shown to possess the ability to produce molecular oxygen when illuminated in the presence of a variety of electron acceptors. The relative nonspecificity for these electron acceptors suggests a nonenzymatic process as the primary mechanism of electron transfer. The apparent requirement of a minimum size for the photochemical apparatus,[125] together with the high degree of organization of units of this same scale indicated by electron microscopy,[107,115] when coupled with the previously educed[95] argument, suggests the presence of a quasi-crystalline lattice [Fig. 20(a), (b), (c)][62] containing, among other things, chlorophyll molecules as the core of the photochemical apparatus. This lattice may have electronic energy levels whose characteristics are determined not by the individual molecules alone, but by their relation to each other as well; that is, they may have properties resembling those of a photo semiconductor.

It is as yet difficult to decide whether one should conceive of the light absorption act as directly producing electrons which can migrate until trapped, or whether this absorption process leads to the formation of neutral migrating excitons which are converted to ion pairs at suitable points in the lattice. This conception resembles an earlier one, derived from kinetic studies, of a "photosynthetic unit"[25,44,45] in which the light absorption is in effect accomplished by an aggregate

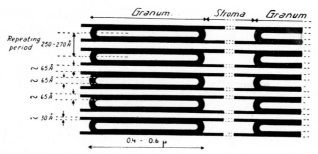

Fig. 20(a). Ultrastructure of chloroplasts according to Steinman and Sjöstrand.

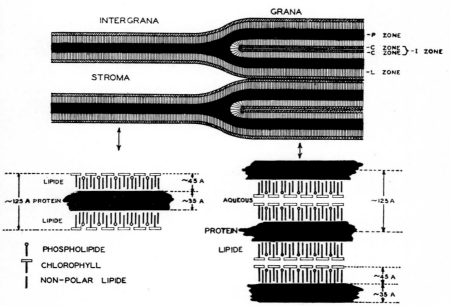

Fig. 20(b). Diagrammatic representation of lamellar structure in the mesophyll chloroplast of *Zea mays*. At top is a representation of the density observed in sections of oxmium-fixed material, at bottom, an interpretation of this in terms of protein, lipide, and chlorophyll. The structure of the lamellae in the parenchyma sheath chloroplasts is indistinguishable from that of the intergrana lamellae of the mesophyll chloroplasts. Drawing not to scale. (According to A. J. Hodge, J. D. McLean, and F. V. Mercer.)

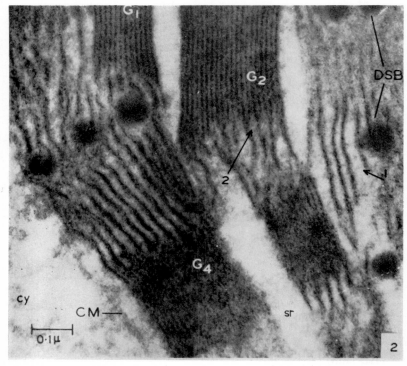

Fig. 20(c). Portion of a mesophyll chloroplast from a 3- to 4-week-old maize leaf. G_1 and G_2, cross section of grana; G_4, oblique section of grana; *arrow 1*, compound nature of lamellae; *arrow 2*, forking at the periphery of the granum; *DSB*, dense spherical bodies; *CM*, limiting membrane; *cy*, cytoplasm; *sr*, stroma (finely granular matrix) of chloroplast.

of several thousand chlorophyll molecules rather than individual ones. The electrons and positive ions produced by either of the afore-mentioned processes are separately trapped at suitable points of differentiation in the lattice. For example: the positive ions or "holes" might exist as oxidized heme components of suitable potential. These can regain their electrons directly from water molecules or from some hydrated species (for example, carotenoid alcohols) which could then lead to molecular oxygen.

One can further visualize a built-in potential gradient which would lead to a diffusional separation of the charge and thus to a separation of the oxidized and the reduced entities. One or the other of these could then be "stored" for appreciable lengths of time (milliseconds to seconds) before being accepted (for electrons) or neutralized (for holes) and the purely chemical stages initiated. Up to some point this process should be reversible, and therefore should show some emission of chlorophyll phosphorescence as has been observed by Strehler.[2,118,119]

On the basis of such observations together with a kinetic analysis of the effect of added lipoic acid upon the efficiency of the Hill

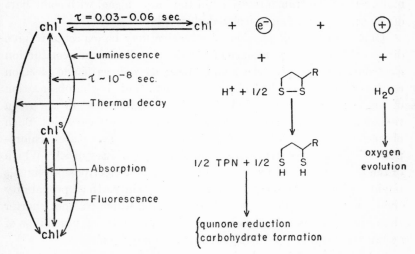

Fig. 21. Scheme for light energy conversion through charge separation.

reaction of *Scenedesmus* cells in flashing light, the following detailed proposal of a sequence of events lying between light absorption and chemical potential has been proposed[24] (Fig. 21).

In this scheme the neutralization of holes by electron donation from water or a hydrated compound is supposed rapid compared to the removal of the trapped electrons by natural oxidants. It seems to us significant that a very similar sequence was devised quite independently to account for an entirely different type of data (fluorescence behavior) by Katz.[72]

One may expect other directly observable physical manifestations of such a system; i.e., the absorption spectrum in the visible region may be expected to show a variety of transient changes associated with each of the successive steps outlined above, followed by slower changes which would be expected of the "purely chemical" transformations which follow. Such changes have been observed by a number of people.[42,43,85,140,141] The most recent of these[140,141] involves observations on isolated chloroplast fragments (grana) in the time region of 10^{-4} second. In this work it was demonstrated that the spectral changes observed clearly demonstrated at least two, and probably more, successive transformations in the intact algae, with some part of the series remaining in isolated chloroplasts.

One other type of physical observation may be expected to give direct evidence of the presence of "triplet state" excitons, conduction electrons, trapped electrons, and holes; as well as single electron carriers in the succeeding chemical system. This is the observation of the possible presence of electron spin resonance[70,136] in the green tissues and its response to illumination and other variables. Such observations have, in fact, already been made in isolated chloroplasts,[37,113] and on partially dried leaf tissue of various types.[113] Which of the above-mentioned sequence of events these electron spin signals might be due to it is too early to say with certainty. In all probability the time of observation in these experiments, which was not shorter than several seconds in either case, would preclude the possibility of seeing effects associated solely with the primary acts.

A method which might be expected to separate the photoelectronic processes from the succeeding chemical transformations would be to make observations at very low temperatures ($< -100°C$) where chemical processes would be expected to proceed extremely slowly. One may confidently expect all enzymatic processes which normally function in the room temperature range to cease in this range of temperatures. We[113] have been able to observe the appearance of an electron spin resonance signal (at $g \simeq 2.0$) immediately upon the illumination of isolated chloroplasts at $-120°C$, with light from a tungsten lamp filtered through plate glass (~ 4 mm.), water (~ 2 cm.), and infrared absorbing glass (~ 2 mm.). This signal was saturated upon first observation ($\simeq 1$ minute) and remained unchanged in the dark as long as the chloroplasts were frozen. After thawing in the dark at room temperature and refreezing, the signal was gone and could be regenerated by illumination. The nature of the signals that are seen are shown in Fig. 22, and a summary of

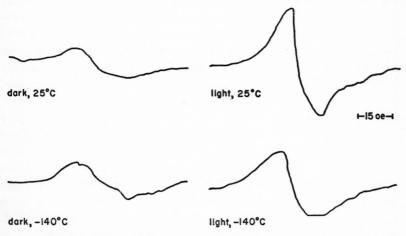

Fig. 22. Spin resonance spectra from wet, large chlorophyll samples.

the various observations that have been made are shown in Table V.[113] This appears to be strong direct evidence for the existence and functioning in the chloroplasts of a system capable of converting electromagnetic energy absorbed by chlorophyll into trapped electrons of high potential by a photoconductive process. It should be

Table V. ELECTRON SPIN RESONANCE OBSERVATIONS ON VARIOUS SAMPLES FROM PHOTOSYNTHETIC MATERIAL. At room temperature, the width between points of maximum slope is approximately 10 oersted; at $-140°$, the width between points of maximum slope is approximately 15 oersteds. Light quality: 5800 $< \lambda < 8000$ Å. Resonance g value is 2.00.

Substance	Light intensity	Temperature	Signal growth time	Signal decay time
Dried leaves..........	low[a]	25°	minutes	hours
Dried whole chloro-plasts..............	low[a]	25°	minutes	hours
		60°[d]	seconds	seconds
Wet whole chloroplasts	low[a]	25°	seconds	~ 1 minute
		$-140°$	seconds	hours
Wet small chloroplast fragments..........	low[a]	25°	seconds	minutes
Wet large chloroplast fragments..........	low[a]	25°	~ 30 seconds	~ 30 seconds
	high[b]	25°	~ 6 seconds	~ 30 seconds
	high[b]	$-140°$	~ 10 seconds	hours[c]

[a] Low light intensity: approximately 10^{15} quanta/sec. into cavity; the number of free electrons at equilibrium was approximately 10^{16}.

[b] High light intensity: approximately 10^{16} quanta/sec. into cavity; the number of free electrons at equilibrium was approximately 10^{16}.

[c] The signal began to disappear rapidly when the temperature was raised to about $> -50°$.

[d] This seems to correspond to the temperature at which there is a peak in the thermoluminescence curve. Observed by G. Tollin in this laboratory in an experiment similar to that described by W. Arnold and H. K. Sherwood.[1]

noted in this connection, that while direct observation of photoconduction in dried chloroplasts has not yet been observed[1] thermoluminescence and semiconduction properties attributable to such a trapping system have been described.[1] On the other hand, it has been possible to demonstrate an increase in conductivity upon illumination of thin films of crude chlorophyll prepared by evaporation of the usual petroleum ether and alcohol extracts.[80]

It is interesting to note that the more precise studies of the thermoconduction, photoconduction, luminescence, and absorption properties of model systems (pure crystals and mixed crystals of aromatic condensed ring systems)[94] have led to the same interpretation for these processes as has the one proposed here to be operative in photosynthesis. In the pure crystals the process is formulated as:

$$h\nu \longrightarrow \text{excited singlet} \longrightarrow \text{triplet} \longrightarrow \text{exciton migration}$$
$$\longrightarrow \text{ionization} \longrightarrow \text{conduction bands}$$

In the crystal containing impurities in which the unperturbed triplet lies below that of the host molecules the process is the same except that the exciton migration leads to trapping and ionization in the impurity levels rather than in the host molecules.

Finally there is the possibility of a refinement of the electron spin resonance type of observation which might permit an unequivocal demonstration of the presence of relatively large volumes of regular organized material in which a conduction (free) electron could move, as contrasted to free radicals of individual molecules (of chlorophyll, flavin, cytochromes, pyridine nucleotides, etc.). This is the method of "cyclotron resonance"[41] which, if demonstrated in such material as chloroplasts or grana, would constitute very strong positive evidence for the type of phenomenon we propose.

XIII

Oxygen Evolution System

So far we have discussed the transfer of the reducing electrons and some possible modes of their creation. It is, of course, clear that for each equivalent of such reducing electrons there must simultaneously be created an equivalent of "holes" or oxidizing agent which can ultimately become molecular oxygen (in green plants). Some information on the origin of this molecular oxygen is available to us from the original isotope studies of Ruben,[106] using O^{18} and following the suggestion of van Niel.[130] This has clearly indicated that this oxygen has its ultimate origin in the oxygen atoms of H_2O. Nothing further is known of the path of oxygen from water to molecular oxygen.

$$H_2O \longrightarrow ? \longrightarrow ? \longrightarrow ? \longrightarrow O_2$$

Among suggestions made is one involving the carotenoids[36,40] but the isotopic evidence is not yet available. Further developments here await the more ready availability of greater amounts and more highly enriched isotopic oxygen O^{18} or O^{17} or both. Also, better methods of detection and analysis are presently being developed which may confidently be expected to provide some of the missing links in this area.

References

1. Arnold, W. and Sherwood, H. K.: "Are Chloroplasts Semiconductors?" *Proc. Nat. Acad. Sci. U. S.*, **43**, 105-114 (1957).

2. Arnold, W. and Thompson, J.: "Delayed Light Production by Blue-Green Algae, Red Algae and Purple Bacteria," *J. Gen. Physiol.*, **39**, 311-318 (1956).

3. Arnon, D. I.: "Glyceraldehyde Phosphate Dehydrogenase of Green Plants," *Science*, **116**, 635-637 (1952).

4. Aronoff, S.: "Metabolism of Soy Bean Leaves. III. The Organic Acids Produced in Short-Time Photosynthesis," *Arch. Biochem. and Biophys.*, **32**, 237-248 (1951).

5. Aronoff, S., Barker, H. A., and Calvin, M.: "Distribution of Labeled Carbon in Sugar from Barley," *J. Biol. Chem.*, **169**, 459-460 (1947).

6. Aronoff, S. and Vernon, L.: "Metabolism of Soybean Leaves. I. The Sequence of Formation of the Soluble Carbohydrates during Photosynthesis," *Arch. Biochem.*, **28**, 424-439 (1950).

7. Axelrod, B. and Bandurski, R. S.: "Phosphoglyceryl Kinase in Higher Plants," *J. Biol. Chem.*, **204**, 939-948 (1953).

8. Axelrod, B. and Jang, R.: "Purification and Properties of Phosphoriboisomerase from Alfalfa," *J. Biol. Chem.*, **209**, 847-855 (1954).

9. Baeyer, A.: "Ueber die Wasserentziehung urd ihre Bedeutung für das Pflanzenleben und die Gährung," *Ber. deut. chem. Ges.*, **3**, 63-75 (1870). Reviewed in *Photosynthesis and Related Proc-*

esses, I, E. I. Rabinowitch, New York. Interscience Publishers, p. 246 (1945).

10. Barker, S. A., Bassham, J. A., Calvin, M., and Quarck, U. C.: "Sites of Azaserine Inhibition during Photosynthesis by *Scenedesmus*," *J. Am. Chem. Soc.*, **78**, 4632-4635 (1956).

11. Barltrop, J. A., Hayes, P. M., and Calvin, M.: "The Chemistry of 1,2-Dithiolane (Trimethylene Disulfide) as the Model for the Primary Quantum Conversion Act in Photosynthesis," *J. Am. Chem. Soc.*, **76**, 4348-4367 (1954).

12. Bassham, J. A., Benson, A. A., and Calvin, M.: "Path of Carbon in Photosynthesis. VIII. The Role of Malic Acid," *J. Biol. Chem.*, **185**, 781-787 (1950).

13. Bassham, J. A., Benson, A. A., Kay, L. D., Harris, A. Z., Wilson, A. T., and Calvin, M.: "The Path of Carbon in Photosynthesis. XXI. The Cyclic Regeneration of Carbon Dioxide Acceptor," *J. Am. Chem. Soc.*, **76**, 1760-1770 (1954).

14. Bassham, J. A., Shibata, K., Steenberg, K., Bourdon, J., and Calvin, M.: "Photosynthetic Cycle and Respiration: Light and Dark Transients," *J. Am. Chem. Soc.*, **78**, 4120-4124 (1956).

15. Benson, A. A. and Bassham, J. A.: "Chemical Degradation of Isotopic Succinic and Malic Acids," *J. Am. Chem. Soc.*, **70**, 3939-3940 (1948).

16. Benson, A. A., Bassham, J. A., Calvin, M., Goodale, T. C., Haas, V. A., and Stepka, W.: "The Path of Carbon in Photosynthesis. V. Paper Chromatography and Radioautography of the Products," *J. Am. Chem. Soc.*, **72**, 1710-1718 (1950).

17. Benson, A. A., Bassham, J. A., Calvin, M., Hall, A. G., Hirsch, H. E., Kawaguchi, S., Lynch, V., and Tolbert, N. E.: "The Path of Carbon in Photosynthesis. XV. Ribulose and Sedoheptulose," *J. Biol. Chem.*, **196**, 703-716 (1952).

18. Benson, A. A. and Calvin, M.: "The Dark Reduction of Photosynthesis," *Science*, **105**, 648-649 (1947).

19. Benson, A. A. and Calvin, M.: "Intermediates of Photosynthesis: Isolation and Degradation Methods," *University of Califor-*

nia, Radiation Laboratory Report, No. 2682, Berkeley, Calif. (1954).

20. Benson, A. A., Calvin, M., Haas, V. A., Aronoff, S., Hall, A. G., Bassham, J. A., and Weigl, J. W.: "C^{14} in Photosynthesis," in *Photosynthesis in Plants* edited by J. Franck and W. Loomis, Iowa. Iowa State College Press, 381-401 (1949).

21. Benson, A. A., Kawaguchi, S., Hayes, P., and Calvin, M.: "The Path of Carbon in Photosynthesis. XVI. Kinetic Relationships of the Intermediates in Steady State Photosynthesis," *J. Am. Chem. Soc.*, **74,** 4477-4482 (1952).

22. Blackman, F. F. and Mattaei, G. L. G.: "Experimental Researches in Vegetable Assimilation and Respiration. IV. A Quantitative Study of Carbon-Dioxide Assimilation and Leaf-Temperature in Natural Illumination," *Proc. Roy. Soc.* (London), **B76,** 402-445 (1905). Reviewed in *Photosynthesis and Related Processes,* I, E. I. Rabinowitch, New York. Interscience Publishers, 172 (1945).

23. Block, R. J., Durrum, E. L., and Zweig, G.: *A Manual of Paper Chromatography and Paper Electrophoresis,* New York. Academic Press Inc. (1955).

24. Bradley, D. F. and Calvin, M.: "The Effect of Thioctic Acid on the Quantum Efficiency of the Hill Reaction in Intermittent Light," *Proc. Nat. Acad. Sci. U. S.*, **41,** 563-571 (1955).

25. Briggs, G. E.: "Photosynthesis in Intermittent Illumination," *Proc. Roy. Soc.* (London), **B130,** 24-31 (1941).

26. Brockman, J. A., Stokstad, E. L. R., Patterson, E. L., Pierce, J. W., and Macchi, M. E.: "Proposed Structures for Protogen-A and Protogen-B," *J. Am. Chem. Soc.*, **76,** 1827-1828 (1954).

27. Buchanan, J. G.: "The Path of Carbon in Photosynthesis. XIX. The Identification of Sucrose Phosphate in Sugar Beet Leaves," *Arch. Biochem. and Biophys.*, **44,** 140-149 (1953).

28. Buchanan, J. G., Bassham, J. A., Benson, A. A., Bradley, D. F., Calvin, M., Daus, L. L., Goodman, M., Hayes, P. M., Lynch, V. H., Norris, L. T., and Wilson, A. T.: "The Path of Carbon

in Photosynthesis. XVII. Phosphorous Compounds as Intermediates in Photosynthesis," in *Phosphorous Metabolism*, II,
Baltimore, Md. Johns Hopkins Press, 440-459 (1952).

29. Burma, D. P. and Mortimer, D. C.: "The Biosynthesis of Uridine Diphosphate Glucose and Sucrose in Sugar Beet Leaf,"
Arch. Biochem. and Biophys., **62**, 16-28 (1956).

30. Burton, K.: "Free Energy Change Associated with the Hydrolysis of the Thiol Ester Bond of Acetyl Coenzyme A," *Biochem. J.*,
59, 44-46 (1955).

31. Burton, K. and Krebs, H. A.: "Free-energy Changes Associated
with the Individual Steps of the Tricarboxylic Acid Cycle,
Glycolysis and Alcoholic Fermentation and with the Hydrolysis
of the Pyrophosphate Groups of the Adenosine Triphosphate,"
Biochem. J., **54**, 94-107 (1953).

32. Burton, K. and Wilson, T. H.: "The Free-energy Changes for
the Reduction of Phosphopyridine Nucleotide and the Dehy-
drogenation of L-Malate and L-Glycerol-1-Phosphate," *Biochem. J.*, **54**, 86-94 (1953).

33. Calvin, M., Bassham, J. A., Benson, A. A., Lynch, V. H.,
Ouellet, C., Schou, L., Stepka, W., and Tolbert, N. E.: "Carbon
Dioxide Assimilation in Plants," *Symposia Soc. Exptl. Biol.*,
V, 284-305 (1951).

34. Calvin, M. and Benson, A. A.: "The Path of Carbon in Photosynthesis," *Science*, **107**, 476-480 (1948).

35. Calvin, M. and Massini, P.: "The Path of Carbon in Photosynthesis. XX. The Steady State," *Experientia*, **VIII**, 445-457
(1952).

36. Cholnoky, L., Györgyfy, C., Nagy, E., and Panczei, M.: "Function of Carotenoids in Chlorophyll-Containing Organs," *Nature*,
178, 410-411 (1956).

37. Commoner, B., Heise, J. J., and Townsend, J.: "Light-Induced
Paramagnetism in Chloroplasts," *Proc. Nat. Acad. Sci. U. S.*,
42, 710-718 (1956).

38. Consden, R., Gordon, A. H., and Martin, A. J. P.: "Qualitative

Analysis of Proteins: A Partition Chromatographic Method Using Paper," *Biochem. J.*, **38**, 224-232 (1944).

39. de Saussure, N. Th.: *Recherches chimiques sur la végétation*, Paris Nyon (1804). Reviewed in *Photosynthesis and Related Processes*, I, E. I. Rabinowitch, New York. Interscience Publishers, 23 (1945).

40. Dorough, G. D. and Calvin, M.: "The Path of Oxygen in Photosynthesis," *J. Am. Chem. Soc.*, **73**, 2362-2364 (1951).

41. Dresselhaus, G., Kip, A. F., and Kittel, C.: "Cyclotron Resonance of Electrons and Holes in Silicon and Germanium Crystals," *Phys. Rev.* **98**, 368-384 (1955).

42. Duysens, L. N. M.: "Transfer of Light Energy within Pigment Systems Present in Photosynthesizing Cells," *Nature*, **168**, 548 (1951).

43. Duysens, L. N. M.: "Reversible Photo-oxidation of a Cytochrome Pigment in Photosynthesizing *Rhodospirillum rubrum*," *Nature*, **173**, 692 (1954).

44. Emerson, R. and Arnold, W.: "Photochemical Reactions in Photosynthesis," *J. Gen. Physiol.*, **16**, 191-205 (1932).

45. Emerson, R. and Arnold, W.: "A Separation of the Reactions in Photosynthesis by Means of Intermittent Light," *J. Gen. Physiol.*, **15**, 391-420 (1932).

46. Gaffron, H.: "Wirkung von Blausäure und Wasserstoffperoxyd auf die Blackmansche Reaktion in *Scenedesmus*," *Biochem. Z.*, **292**, 241-270 (1937).

47. Gaffron, H.: "Über auffalende Unterschiede in der Physiologie nahe verwandter Algenstämme, nebst Bemerkungen über Lichtatmung," *Biol. Zentr.*, **59**, 302-313 (1939).

48. Gaffron, H., Fager, E. W., and Brown, A.: "The C^{14}-Labeled Products of the Aerobic and Anaerobic Light and Dark Reactions of Photosynthesis as Fractionated with Benzene Alcohol," in a panel discussion "Plant Metabolism and Photosynthesis" at Symposium on the Uses of Isotopes in Biology and Medicine, University of Wisconsin, Madison, Wisconsin (1947).

49. Gibbs, M.: "Triose Phosphate Dehydrogenase and Glucose 6-Phosphate Dehydrogenase in the Pea Plant," *Nature*, **170**, 164 (1952).

50. Gibbs, M. and Kandler, O.: "Asymmetric Distribution of C^{14} in Sugars Formed during Photosynthesis," *Plant Physiol.*, **31**, 411-412, *Proc. Nat. Acad. Sci. U. S.*, **43**, 446-451 (1957).

51. Gomori, G.: "Hexosedi Phosphatase," *J. Biol. Chem.*, **148**, 139-149 (1943).

52. Gunsalus, I. C.: In McCollum Pratt Institute Symposium on "Mechanism of Enzyme Action" Baltimore, Md. Johns Hopkins University Press (1954).

53. Gunsalus, I. C. and Gibbs, M.: "The Heterolactic Fermentation. II. Position of C^{14} in the Products of the Glucose Dissimilation by *Leuconostoc mesenteroides*," *J. Biol. Chem.*, **194**, 871-875 (1952).

54. Gunsalus, I. C., Struglis, L., and O'Kane, D. I.: "Pyruvic Acid Metabolism. IV. Occurrence, Properties, and Partial Purification of Pyruvate Oxidation Factor," *J. Biol. Chem.*, **194**, 859-869 (1952).

55. Hagerman, R. H. and Arnon, D. I.: "Changes in Glyceraldehyde Phosphate Dehydrogenase during the Life Cycle of a Green Plant," *Arch. Biochem. and Biophys.*, **57**, 421-436 (1955).

56. Hartman, S. C., Levenberg, B., and Buchanan, J. M.: "Involvement of ATP, 5-Phosphoribosylpyrophosphate and L-Azaserine in the Enzymatic Formation of Glycinamide Ribotide Intermediates in Inosinic Acid Biosynthesis," *J. Am. Chem. Soc.*, **77**, 501-503 (1955).

57. Hassid, W. Z., Doudoroff, M., and Barker, H. A.: "Enzymatically Synthesized Crystalline Sucrose," *J. Am. Chem. Soc.*, **66**, 1416-1419 (1944).

58. Havinga, E., Lynch, V., Norris, L., and Calvin, M.: "The Effect of Certain Biologically Active Substances upon Photosynthesis and Dark CO_2 Fixation," *Rec. trav. chim.*, **72**, 597-611 (1953).

59. Hill, R.: "Oxygen Evolved by Isolated Chloroplasts," *Nature*, **139**, 881-882 (1937).

60. Hill, R. and Scarisbrick, R.: "The Reduction of Ferric Oxalate by Isolated Chloroplasts," *Proc. Roy. Soc.* (London), **B129**, 238-255 (1940).

61. Hill, R. and Scarisbrick, R.: "Production of Oxygen by Illuminated Chloroplasts," *Nature*, **146**, 61-62 (1940).

62. Hodge, A. J., McLean, J. D., and Mercer, F. V.: "Ultrastructure of the Lamellae and Grana in the Chloroplasts of *Zea Mays L*," *J. Biophys. Biochem. Cyt.*, **1**, 605-614 (1955).

63. Horecker, B. L. and Smyrniotis, P. Z.: "Transaldolase: The Formation of Fructose-6-Phosphate from Sedoheptulose-7-Phosphate," *J. Am. Chem. Soc.*, **75**, 2021-2022 (1953).

64. Horecker, B. L., Smyrniotis, P. Z., and Klenow, H.: "The Formation of Sedoheptulose Phosphate from Pentose Phosphate," *J. Biol. Chem.*, **205**, 661-682 (1953).

65. Horecker, B. L., Smyrniotis, P. A., and Seegmiller, J. E.: "The Enzymatic Conversion of 6-Phosphogluconate to Ribulose-5-Phosphate and Ribose-5-Phosphate," *J. Biol. Chem.*, **193**, 383-396 (1951).

66. Hough, L. and Jones, J. K. N.: "The Synthesis of Sugars from Simpler Substances, Part V. Enzymic Synthesis of Sedoheptulose," *J. Chem. Soc.* (London), 342-345 (1953).

67. Hurwitz, J., Weissbach, A., Horecker, B. L., and Smyrniotis, P. Z.: "Spinach Phosphoribulokinase," *J. Biol. Chem.*, **218**, 769-783 (1956).

68. Ingen-Housz, J.: *Experiences sur végétables, etc.* (French translation by the author with additions), Paris. F. Didot le jeune (1780). Reviewed in *Photosynthesis and Related Processes*, I, E. I. Rabinowitch, New York. Interscience Publishers, 17 (1945).

69. Ingen-Housz, J.: "Essay on the Food of Plants and the Renovation of Soils" (Appendix to 15th Chapter of the *General Report from the Board of Agriculture*) London (1796). Book in German:

Ernährung der Pflanzen und Fruchtbarkeit des Bodens, Leipzig (1798). Review in *Photosynthesis and Related Processes,* I, E. I. Rabinowitch, New York. Interscience Publishers, 17 (1945).

70. Ingram, D. J. E.: *Spectroscopy at Radio and Microwave Frequencies,* London. Butterworth, Ltd. (1955).

71. Jakoby, W. G., Brummond, D. O., and Ochoa, S.: "Formation of 3-Phosphoglyceric Acid by Carbon Dioxide Fixation with Spinach Leaf Enzymes," *J. Biol. Chem.,* **218,** 811-822 (1956).

72. Katz, E.: "Chlorophyll Fluorescence as an Energy Flowmeter for Photosynthesis," in *Photosynthesis in Plants,* Iowa State College Press, 287-292 (1949).

73. Kandler, O.: "A Cyanide Insensitive Light Phosphorylation in *Chlorella,*" *Plant Physiol.,* **31,** xvii-xviii (1956).

74. Kandler, O.: "Alcohol and KCN Poisoning in Short-Time Photosynthesis Studies," *University of California Radiation Laboratory Report 3710,* 9-20 (March 1957).

75. Kandler, O. and Gibbs, M.: "Asymmetric Distribution of C[14] in the Glucose Phosphates formed during Photosynthesis," *Plant Physiol.,* **31,** 411-412 (1956).

76. Kluyver, A. J. and Donker, H. J. L.: "Die Einheit in der Biochemie," *Chem. Zelle. Gewebe.,* **13,** 134-190 (1926).

77. Kornberg, A.: "The Metabolism of Phosphorous-Containing Coenzymes," in *Phosphorous Metabolism,* I, Baltimore, Md. Johns Hopkins University Press, 392-413 (1951).

78. Kornberg, H. L., Quayle, J. R., and Calvin, M.: "Studies on the Carboxylation Reaction of Photosynthesis," *University of California Radiation Laboratory Report 2885,* Berkeley, Calif. (1955).

79. Krebs, H. A. and Johnson, W. A.: "The Roles of Citric Acid in Intermediate Metabolism in Animal Tissues," *Enzymologia,* **4,** 148-156 (1937).

80. LaForce, Richard: Observations in our laboratory (1956).

81. Leloir, L. F. and Cardini, C. E.: "The Biosynthesis of Sucrose Phosphate," *J. Biol. Chem.,* **214,** 157-165 (1955).

82. Levenberg, B. and Buchanan, J. M.: "Formylglycinamidine Ribotide and 5-Amino-Imidazole Ribotide—Intermediates in the Biosynthesis of Inosinic Acid *de novo*," *J. Am. Chem. Soc.*, **78,** 504-505 (1956).

83. Liebig, J.: "Die Wechselwirthschaft," *Ann. Chemie*, **46,** 58-97 (1843). Review in *Photosynthesis and Related Processes*, I, E. I. Rabinowitch, New York. Interscience Publishers, 246 (1945).

84. Linko, P., Holm-Hansen, O., Bassham, J. A., and Calvin, M.: "Formation of Radioactive Citrulline during Photosynthesic $C^{14}O_2$ Fixation by Blue-Green Algae," *J. Exptl. Bot.*, **8,** 147-156 (1957).

85. Lundegårth, H.: "On Oxidation of Cytochrome f by Light," *Physiol. Plantarum*, **7,** 375-382 (1954).

86. Martin, A. J. P. and Synge, R. L. M.: "Separation of the Higher Monoamino-Acids by Counter Liquid-Liquid Extraction: The Amino-Acid Composition of Wool," *Biochem. J.*, **35,** 91-121 (1941).

87. Martin, A. J. P. and Synge, R. L. M.: "A New Form of Chromatogram Employing Two Liquid Phases. 1: A Theory of Chromatography. 2: Application to the Micro-Determination of the Higher Monoamino-Acids in Proteins," *Biochem. J.*, **35,** 1358-1368 (1941).

88. Mayaudon, J., Benson, A. A., and Calvin, M.: "Ribulose-1, 5-Diphosphate and CO_2 Fixation from *Tetragonia expansa* Leaves Extract," *Biochim. et Biophys. Acta*, **23,** 342-351 (1957).

89. Mayer, J. R.: *Die Organische Bewegung in ihrem Zusammenhang mit dem Stoffwechsel*, Heilbronn (1845). Reprinted in *Die Mechanik der Warme; gesammelte Schriften*, Stuttgart (1893) and in Ostwald's *Klassiker der exacten Naturwissenschaften*, No. 180, Leipzig. Akad. Verlagsgesellschaft (1911). Review in *Photosynthesis and Related Processes*, I, E. I. Rabinowitch, New York. Interscience Publishers, 26 (1945).

90. Moses, V.: Work in this laboratory (1957).

91. Myers, J.: "Culture Conditions and the Development of the

Photosynthetic Mechanism. V. Influence of the Composition of the Nutrient Medium," *Plant Physiol.*, **22**, 590-597 (1947).

92. Myers, J.: "The Pattern of Photosynthesis in *Chlorella*," *Photosynthesis in Plants*, Iowa. Iowa State College Press, 349-364 (1949).

93. Norris, L., Norris, R. E., and Calvin, M.: "A Survey of the Rates and Products of Short-Term Photosynthesis in Plants of Nine Phyla," *J. Exptl. Bot.*, **6**, 64-74 (1955).

94. Northrup, D. C. and Simpson, O.: "Electronic Properties of Aromatic Hydrocarbons. I. Electrical Conductivity. II. Fluorescence Transfer in Solid Solutions," *Proc. Roy. Soc.* (London), **A234**, 124-149 (1956).

95. Perner, E. S.: "Die ontogentische der Chloroplasten," *Z. Naturforsch.*, **11b**, 560-566, 567-573 (1956).

96. Priestley, J.: "Observations on Different Kinds of Air," *Phil. Trans. Roy. Soc.* (London), **62**, 147-264 (1772). Review in *Photosynthesis and Related Processes*, I, E. I. Rabinowitch, New York. Interscience Publishers, 14 (1945).

97. Putman, E. W.: "Sugar Transformations in the Leaves of *Cannaindica*," Ph.D. Thesis, University of California, Berkeley, Calif. (1952).

98. Quayle, J. R., Fuller, R. C., Benson, A. A., and Calvin, M.: "Enzymatic Carboxylation of Ribulose Diphosphate," *J. Am. Chem. Soc.*, **76**, 3610-3611 (1954).

99. Rabin, B., Pon, N., Shaw, D., and Anderson, J.: Work in this laboratory. O. Kandler, private communication (1957).

100. Racker, E.: "Synthesis of Carbohydrates from Carbon Dioxide and Hydrogen in a Cell-Free System," *Nature*, **175**, 249-251 (1955).

101. Racker, E., de la Haba, G., and Leder, I. G.: "Thiamine Pyrophosphate, A Coenzyme of Transketolase," *J. Am. Chem. Soc.*, **75**, 1010-1011 (1953).

102. Ruben, S., Hassid, W. Z., and Kamen, M. D.: "Radioactive Carbon in the Study of Photosynthesis," *J. Am. Chem. Soc.*, **61**, 661-663 (1939).

103. Ruben, S. and Kamen, M. D.: "Photosynthesis with Radioactive Carbon. IV. Molecular Weight of the Intermediate Products and a Tentative Theory of Photosynthesis," *J. Am. Chem. Soc.*, **62**, 3451-3455 (1940).

104. Ruben, S. and Kamen, M. D.: "Radioactive Carbon in the Study of Respiration in Heterotrophic Systems," *Proc. Nat. Acad. Sci. U. S.*, **26**, 418-426 (1940).

105. Ruben, S. and Kamen, M. D.: "Nonphotochemical Reduction of Carbon Dioxide by Biological Systems," *J. Applied Phys.*, **12**, 321-322 (1941).

106. Ruben, S., Randall, M., Kamen, M., and Hyde, J. L.: "Heavy Oxygen (O^{18}) as a Tracer in the Study of Photosynthesis," *J. Am. Chem. Soc.*, **63**, 877-879 (1941).

107. Sager, R. and Palade, G. E.: "Chloroplast Structure in Green and Yellow Strains of *Chlamydomonas*," *Exptl. Cell Res.*, **7**, 584-588 (1954).

108. Sanadi, D. R. and Searls, R. L.: "Reactions of Thioctic Acid and Thioctamide Catalyzed by the Alpha-Ketoglutaric Dehydrogenase Complex." *Federation Proc.*, 241 (1957).

109. Schou, L., Benson, A. A., Bassham, J. A., and Calvin, M.: "The Path of Carbon in Photosynthesis. XI. The Role of Glycolic Acid," *Physiol. Plantarum*, **3**, 487-495 (1950).

110. Senebier, J.: *Mémoires physico-chimiques sur l'influence de la lumière solaire pour modifier les êtres de trois règnes, surtout ceux du règne végétal*, 3 Vols., Genève. Chirol (1782). Review in *Photosynthesis and Related Processes*, I, E. I. Rabinowitch, New York. Interscience Publishers, 19 (1945).

111. Shaw, D., Rabin, B., Pon, N., and Anderson, J.: Work in this laboratory (1957).

112. Smith, G. E.: *Cerate Oxidimetry*, Columbus, Ohio. G. Frederick Smith Chemical Co. (1942).

113. Sogo, P. B., Pon, N., and Calvin, M.: "Photo Spin Resonance in Chlorophyll-Containing Plant Material," *Proc. Nat. Acad. Sci. U. S.*, **43**, 387-393 (1957). Calvin, M. and Sogo, P. B.: "Pri-

mary Quantum Conversion Process in Photosynthesis: Electron
Spin Resonance." *Science*, **125**, 499-500 (1957).

114. Srere, P. A., Cooper, J. R., Klybas, V., and Racker, E.: "Xylu-
lose-5-Phosphate, A New Intermediate in the Pentose Phosphate
Cycle," *Arch. Biochem. and Biophys.*, **59**, 535-538 (1955).

115. Steinman, E. and Sjöstrand, F. S.: "The Ultrastructure of the
Chloroplast," *Exptl. Cell Res.*, **8**, 15-23 (1955).

116. Stepka, W., Benson, A. A., and Calvin, M.: "The Path of Carbon in Photosynthesis. II. Amino Acids," *Science*, **108**, 304
(1948).

117. Stokstad, E. L. F., Hoffman, C. E., Regan, M. A., Fordham, D.,
and Jukes, T. H.: "Observations on an Unknown Growth Factor
Essential for *Tetrahymena geleii*," *Arch. Biochem.*, **20**, 75-82
(1949).

118. Strehler, B. L.: "The Luminescence of Isolated Chloroplasts,"
Arch. Biochem. and Biophys., **34**, 239-248 (1951).

119. Strehler, B. L. and Arnold, W.: "Light Production by Green
Plants," *J. Gen. Physiol.*, 809-820 (1951).

120. Stumpf, P. K.: "Carbohydrate Metabolism in Higher Plants.
I. Pea Aldolase," *J. Biol. Chem.*, **176**, 233-241 (1948).

121. Stumpf, P. K.: "Carbohydrate Metabolism in Higher Plants.
III. Breakdown of Fructose Diphosphate by Pea Extracts,"
J. Biol. Chem., **182**, 261-272 (1950).

122. Stumpf, P. K. and Horecker, B. L.: "The Role of Xylulose-5-
Phosphate in Xylulose Metabolism of *Lactobacillus pentosus*,"
J. Biol. Chem., **218**, 753-768 (1956).

123. Tewfic, S. and Stumpf, P. K.: "Carbohydrate Metabolism in
Higher Plants. II. The Distribution of Aldolase in Plants,"
Am. J. Bot., **36**, 567-571 (1949).

124. Tewfic, S. and Stumpf, P. K.: "Carbohydrate Metabolism in
Higher Plants. IV. Observations in Triose Phosphate Dehydrogenase," *J. Biol. Chem.*, **192**, 519-526 (1951).

125. Thomas, J. B., Blaauw, O. H., and Duysens, L. N. M.: "On

the Relation between Size and Photochemical Activity of Fragments of Spinach Grana," *Biochim. et Biophys. Acta*, **10**, 230-240 (1953).

126. Thunberg, T.: "Über einen neuen Weg von der Kohlensäure zum Formaldehyd. Ein Beitrag zur Theorie der Kohlensäureassimilation," *Z. Physik. Chem.*, **106**, 305-312 (1923).

127. Topper, Y. J. and Hastings, A. B.: "A Study of the Chemical Origins of Glycogen by Use of C^{14}-Labeled Carbon Dioxide, Acetate, and Pyruvate," *J. Biol. Chem.*, **179**, 1255 (1949).

128. van der Meulen, P. Y. F. and Bassham, J. A.: "Influence of 6-Diazo-5-Oxonorleucine on the Metabolism of *Scenedesmus* and *Chlorella* during Photosynthesis," *University of California Radiation Laboratory Report 3595*, 33 (1956).

129. van Niel, C. B.: "On the Morphology and Physiology of the Purple and Green Sulfur Bacteria," *Arch. Mikrobiol.*, **3**, 1-112 (1931).

130. van Niel, C. B.: "The Bacterial Photosyntheses and Their Importance for the General Problems of Photosynthesis," *Adv. Enzymol.*, **I**, 263-328 (1941).

131. Weinhouse, S., Medes, G., and Floyd, N. F.: "Fatty Acid Metabolism. V. The Conversion of Fatty Acid Intermediates to Citrate, Studied with the Aid of Isotopic Carbon," *J. Biol. Chem.*, **166**, 691-703 (1946).

132. Weissbach, A. and Horecker, B. L.: "Enzymatic Formation of Phosphoglyceric Acid from Ribulose Diphosphate and CO_2," *Federation Proc.*, **14**, 302-303 (1955).

133. Weissbach, A., Horecker, B. L., and Hurwitz, J.: "The Enzymatic Formation of Phosphoglyceric Acid from Ribulose Diphosphate and Carbon Dioxide," *J. Biol. Chem.*, **218**, 795-810 (1956).

134. Weissbach, A., Smyrniotis, P. Z., and Horecker, B. L.: "Pentose Phosphate and CO_2 Fixation with Spinach Extracts," *J. Am. Chem. Soc.*, **76**, 3611-3612 (1954).

135. Weissbach, A., Smyrniotis, P. A., and Horecker, B. L.: "The

Enzymatic Formulation of Ribulose Diphosphate," *J. Am. Chem. Soc.*, **76**, 5572-5573 (1954).

136. Wertz, J. E.: "Nuclear and Electronic Spin Magnetic Resonance. Part II. Electron Spin Resonance of Nearly Free Dipoles," *Chem. Revs.*, **55**, 901-955 (1955).

137. Wieland, H.: "Über den Mechanismus der Oxydationvorgänge (III)," *Ber deut. chem. Ges.*, **47**, 2085-2111 (1914).

138. Willstätter, R. and Stoll, A.: *Untersuchungen über die Assimilation der Kohlensäure*, Berlin. Springer (1918). Review in *Photosynthesis and Related Processes*, E. I. Rabinowitch, New York. Interscience Publishers, 172 (1945).

139. Wilson, A. T. and Calvin, M.: "The Photosynthetic Cycle. CO_2 Dependent Transients," *J. Am. Chem. Soc.*, **77**, 5948-5957 (1955).

140. Witt, H. T.: "Experimente zum Primärprozeß der Photosynthese," *Z. Elektrochem.*, **59**, 981-986 (1955).

141. Witt, H. T., Morwaw, R., and Muller, A.: "Voränge im Primärprozeß der Photosynthese," *Angew. Chem.*, **68**, 495 (1956).

142. Wood, H. G., Lifson, N., and Lorber, V.: "The Position of Fixed Carbon in Glucose from Rat Liver Glycogen," *J. Biol. Chem.*, **159**, 475-489 (1945).